W E

KNEW THESE MEN

Also by WILFRED BRANDON

TRANSCRIBED BY EDITH ELLIS

❖

OPEN THE DOOR!

"How anyone could read it and not be better and wiser for the experience I cannot imagine. . . . For there is true eloquence in it; there is wisdom, there is nobility. . . . The book is thrillingly interesting, even exciting."

—CLAUDE BRAGDON

INCARNATION

A Plea from the Masters

"I think Brandon's books colossal in their importance: a message to the world in the moment of its direst need. If the world ignores that message so much the worse for future generations."

—ALBERT BIGELOW PAINE

THESE ARE *Merit Publications*
Published by
G. & R. ANTHONY, INC.

WE
KNEW THESE MEN

BY

WILFRED BRANDON

TRANSCRIBED BY

EDITH ELLIS

G. & R. ANTHONY, INC.

PUBLISHERS

New York

"A Master Publication"

Fourth Printing, March, 1957

Published simultaneously in Canada by The Ryerson Press

THE TRANSCRIBER

❖

As MASTER and pupil, Author and amanuensis, Wilfred Brandon and I have been associated for ten years. There was nothing in my background or training to forecast it.

My father was a free thinker, a humanist such as Robert Ingersoll, whom he greatly admired and often quoted. He showed no desire to influence his children in this direction or to oppose our mother's views, which were those common to members of the Episcopal Church. We were a theatrical family and our attendance at church service was necessarily intermittent. An early and unpleasant experience at a private séance had made my mother a firm opponent of Spiritualism.

To the age of thirteen my life was mostly in and of the theatre. My reading was largely in my father's books of plays. The ghost in *Hamlet* and the witches in *Macbeth* had no meaning for me except just as characters in a play. When "at liberty" I attended Sunday school, where the many psychic incidents in the Bible lessons were never illuminated for me, and even later they bore no relation in my mind to the practices of the Spiritualists and of mediums. My prejudice against them was inherited and entirely orthodox.

By the time I was full grown I had come to question dogma and take the agnostic view of my father. Afterward came the soul-shaking experience when a loved member of the family is sentenced to pass, in lingering pain, through the dark curtain into the Unknown.

Fate, it would seem, sent me to the house of friends where I was to find Reports of the London Society for Psychic Research for two years, fifty-odd numbers of the occult weekly *Light*, and some books by Stainton Moses, the British clergyman who in starting a crusade to expose and annihilate mediums and Spiritualism found that he himself was an extraordinarily gifted psychic.

Here was hope and more than hope! Here were the names of distinguished men of international fame in their different fields of science and art; men who would not risk their reputations by lending themselves to the protection of charlatanism and fraud. Such men as Camille Flammarion, the French astronomer; Cesare Lombroso, the Italian physician, psychiatrist, and criminologist; Maurice Maeterlinck, the Belgian author; Austrians, Germans and other Continentals. Of the English there were such men as Lord Balfour, then Secretary of the London S.P.R., Professor Sidgwick, Myers, Hodgson, Sir Oliver Lodge, William Stead. If such men, after their exhaustive investigations, could pledge themselves to survial and communication between the two planes of being, who was I to question their conclusions. I knew myself as too imaginative, inexperienced, and emotionally unfitted to investigate on my own account, but the whole question was settled in its main aspects so far as I was concerned.

Death had come again. This time it took my husband. My exterior life became a very busy one. I did not act again, but devoted myself to play-writing and directing. My domestic and professional affairs made too many demands for much esoteric speculation or study. I had become interested in the study of mental and spiritual science and read on these subjects when time permitted, though I was too occupied in earning a living to become absorbed in any belief.

Occasionally and unexpectedly people came to my home who possessed some degree of psychic development. One was an adept in automatic writing. I was curious enough to try it myself, but the pencil would not stir for me. A friend brought a private medium to my apartment, unasked, and she gave an exhibition of her powers. There were both visible and audible manifestations, but they seemed trivial and unimportant.

In order to receive their magazine I became an associate member of the American Society for Psychic Research and for many years have read of the progress of their work and that of others throughout the world. I have not attended their séances or lectures, preferring to study the subject apart and alone. The case for survival has been so completely proved that all that is now needed is to observe the different forms of mediumship and manifestation valuable in establishing classifications of this new and growing science. I am not a scientist, so the work interested me only in its general sense.

During the first World War I was one of those who could feel none of the excitement, patriotic fervour or glory in the slaughter and destruction. The headlines of the press were a daily horror even though no kin of mine was at the front or in action. The revelation of man's cruelty to man made consciousness a burden. I grew weak, listless, and negative.

In the late summer of 1919, while at my typewriter revising a manuscript, scarcely knowing how it happened, I seized a pencil and began to write on the scratch paper beside me. The writing was bold, regular, beautiful, such as I could not hope to imitate. The subject was Survival. I understood what was happening and was interested, even amused. I continued to take this writing down for two or three days. Suddenly I began to *hear*. This terrified me notwithstanding all my reading on the subject. I feared something had happened to my mind.

Soon I recognized my father's voice. He had passed in June 1914, my mother ten years earlier. I heard my father's special name for me and recognized his characteristic phraseology. Then his father came, Dr. Thomas Ellis, who died when I was twelve. I was conscious of his Dublin accent, which I but faintly remembered. My mother spoke to me. My grandfather explained that since I had become clairaudient they were there to protect me against invasion by entities who might try to annoy me. He also said he had secured the help of the powerful mind of a Master who would have charge.

When the next voice spoke I was conscious of a powerful vibration. This was Brandon. He reassured me and said that for a time I was to be in his care.

All this could not have happened at a more inconvenient time. In a month or less I was to start directing rehearsals of a new comedy I had written. I left New York for a village far out on Long Island to rest and solve this problem. Brandon was with me and a helper whom he called Lady West. Often I heard whole conversations between them as well as their occasional words to me.

The night before I left for home Brandon gave me his final instructions to the effect that I was to cease all automatic writing, stop "listening," and shut off everything, devoting myself solely to my own affairs since my responsibilities were too heavy to allow of anything else. We said good-bye and I thanked him for his care. I obeyed these orders to the letter though now and then, probably at a symphony concert, Lady West's voice would suddenly comment on a passage of music that had stirred me deeply. Occasionally there came through a few words of warning, a bit of good council, and once a prophecy that was later fulfilled. That was all. At last even the memory of all this grew so dim as to seem almost unreal. In one of his books Brandon says that for ten years after 1919 I was being prepared for what was to come.

In 1930 I went from New York to Hollywood to write for the screen. While working on an eighteenth-century play there was difficulty in finding a secretary who could take this sort of dictation. At last Miss X was sent to me; she was experienced, cultured, and admirable for the work. After some months of this association I learned that she was not only clairvoyant and clairaudient but a marvelous automatic writer as well. She was reluctant to let this be known, fearing to excite prejudice in her business connection.

Miss X and I were absolute strangers to each other's family history and had no friend in common who could reveal any part of it. By means of her gift for automatic writing I received messages from my grandfather Ellis as well as from my parents. All were so accurate as to signatures and content that I could not doubt their authenticity.

Finally Brandon was the one who took charge of these communications. His ardent plea was for help to send through to the people of the United States a warning of the danger of another World War. He said that Europe still thought war and willed war. This seemed incredible after the tragedy of 1914–18 with its suffering, loss, and futility.

Then my grandfather asked whether I would put myself again in Brandon's care and learn to write automatically for him. This seemed a dangerous chance for me to take. The economic situation was growing worse, the theatre was shrinking. How was I to meet my financial responsibilities? It was a long hard battle with my-self, but something within me would not let me refuse this task. At last I consented, though I exacted a pledge that I should never lose dominion over my mind or be put in a trance. The promise was given and has been kept. At all times since, I've been free to judge and decide and govern my own actions. Though Brandon never interferes in my personal affairs he is meticulous and prop-erly exacting about his own work. I know I have his goodwill and respect for my private and professional life.

First I had to learn to relax my mind and body as I held the pencil. Soon I could take a dozen words, but a few more and the pressure of Brandon's strong mental vibration on the gland at the top and to the right of my spine would become unbearable. If I wished for proof that another mind than my subconscious guided my pencil it was there in the ache at the back of my neck. One's subconscious mind does not ache.

With daily practice my resistance grew along with my facility in receiving. It was a long apprenticeship, in which I was given much valuable teaching and information. When I returned to New York my own affairs demanded my complete attention though I wrote nightly for Brandon to keep in practice. In the West my clairaudi-ence had returned and frequently he would speak to me. This "hearing" is clear in California, less so in the East, and in London I do not hear at all, owing to the difference in strength of the actinic rays of the sun in these localities.

Two years passed before I was able to spare time for the tran-scribing of Wilfred Brandon's first book, *Open the Door!* It was my custom to begin writing at ten o'clock at night and turn out a chapter at a sitting. Often my subconscious mind would try to add to a sentence. When this happened, at the first pause the pencil would move up and Brandon would scratch out the words not his own and write "Relax."

With no erasures or false starts, no means of consulting notes, each chapter would be dictated without hesitation. One wonders when reading his crystal-clear and perfect English if such a thing would be possible for a writer in the mortal world.

Apart from the hours set for writing, if Brandon is present and wishes to send through a message he attracts my attention by directing his mental vibration to a muscle or nerve in the outside of my right palm. This sets up just such a fluttering as one sometimes has in the eyelid.

Unlike Miss X I am not an automatic writer in the true sense, but what Brandon calls a rapport writer. I see and know the words as they are written, but the memory of what they are passes in a few seconds. When I read the whole page it is all new to me. I do not know why this is so.

The work has required many sacrifices on my part as on Brandon's. Still the result for me has been a gain that now I cannot compute. Life has been given a far greater meaning, and most of all I value this opportunity to pass on to others what has made Earthly existence over for me.

EDITH ELLIS

Dedicated to

THE FALLEN IN THE FIRST WORLD WAR

FOREWORD

❖

THE present war in Europe is fast threatening to spread to the United States. There can be but one interest to all Americans— how best to serve those who must face the ultimate issue and possibly the supreme sacrifice. The last war has been a tragedy on both planes of consciousness, yours and ours. It is important that it should not occur again.

It may surprise the reader to find that the author is a citizen of the Astral, or Etheric, plane. This, however, is a fact. I lost my life in 1781 as a soldier in the Continental uniform at the age of nineteen. Since then I have remained in this realm; first employing myself in acquiring a broader education, and for more than a century teaching souls as they arrive.

We are making this effort through the hand of Edith Ellis. We are a close associate of her grandfather, Thomas Ellis, who died when she was a child. He it was who furnished her with the proofs of his identity in 1931. These communications cannot be credited to her own subconscious mind, for it was through a stranger to her own and her family's history that we addressed her for some time, until her doubts were set at rest. Thomas Ellis persuaded her to act as my amanuensis in the hope of aiding in the cause of world peace. While practising her profession as a dramatist she has already permitted me to write two books which are now in print. Doubt may be cast on this method of getting this knowledge to you, but at present there is no other way than the use of the radio activity of a human being. This we who are Masters of Etheric life can use telepathically with the co-operation of a mortal.

There has always been a very great body of evidence as to the survival of the individual. The last war has made it imperative that the truth should now be generally known.

To avert the tragic consequences often attending life after death there are but two things needed: first, an understanding that we cannot die and, second, an insight into what life after death is really like.

All religions, even the most primitive, have held the teaching of immortality, but the knowledge of the natural laws governing it has been withheld. Until recent times the ignorance of the masses made this necessary in order to hold them in check through their fear of the unknown. Modern science and free education have made this system of control not only inefficient but a danger rather than an aid to public order and morals.

We have shown in our two previous books, *Open the Door!* and *Incarnation*, the consequence of sending youth to war with no comprehension of how to use its mental power in its own defence before and after leaving the mortal body. This must not happen again.

In the following chapters I have chosen to get the truth out by showing in speech and action the experiences of the characters in a unit of American soldiers at the front in the last World War.

It was while one of a band of Master spirits who volunteered to go to France to receive the souls of our own dead in 1918 that I came to know the intimate thoughts of our men at the front there; those who survived as well as those who were in our care.

The events, the characters, their conversations and experiences, are all profoundly true. These men I have listened to as they lived their days and nights in the dugouts, the canteens, in the trenches, and on the battlefields. We know them as mortals never can, for we got their thoughts as well as their spoken words.

We know these men after death and the way they carry over their earthly desires. We know the inmates of your hospitals also and the maimed outside them and those whose bodies escaped but whose mentalities and standards were never the same again. We know too the women the soldiers loved and who loved them, living or dead.

We have set down nothing that has not happened except on the last three pages of the book. We have placed the men whose experiences we wished to recount in one unit because this form may impress the general reader more vividly than a scientific and formally written explanation of Etheric life.

We wish only to show how the life of mankind operates when freed from the encasement of flesh. Here we are still men with all the emotions and passions of men and we also have powers that when properly used can make an Etheric career both satisfying and useful.

My purpose is to arm our people with the knowledge supremely needed for their defence. The government cannot give them this equipment along with uniforms, weapons, ammunition, and shelters, for obvious reasons.

Defence of one's country against a robber nation no one can criticize, but we hope that no citizen will be sent to war who has not the information that will enable him to save his mind intact and to use its power in his own behalf. Ignorance of the law brings its penalty on every plane.

We cannot but believe that class war, race war, religious war, and the reign of greed, power-lust, and reckless disregard for human rights would give way to a saner and more tolerant world if it were universally understood that *the living and the dead are all in this together.*

WILFRED BRANDON

New York
Spring, 1941

CHAPTER I

HOW WE KNEW THEM

❖

THE excitement on our plane of life was almost as great as on yours when the United States entered the war in 1917. We knew then that every man among us who was adept in using his mind power must enlist. If our troops were to fight in France there must be spirits to receive their dead. We determined that no American soul should be abandoned to an after life among those alien to him.

We sailed on the ships that carried our soldiers. We received our orders from one of the Master spirits who made his headquarters with that of the A.E.F. Command. We were assigned our posts on the American sectors.

At my station, though I was in charge, twenty Master souls were with me. Since we have no material resources we obtain our title and degree of Master for mastery of our mind, will, and emotions. In the following episodes I have given a different name to the part I played, and for the sake of their families and friends, fictitious ones to the men and women whose stories are told.

How did we know these men so intimately?

We were with them in the dugouts and trenches, in the canteens and hospitals, on the field and in the aftermath. We heard their conversations and telepathically we got their long thoughts. To help souls it is necessary to know them in this way quite as your physicians and psychiatrists must know their patients.

The stories of these seven buck privates are a vivid memory to me. They represent a microcosm of mentalities, a democracy of the ranks unlike in all but their uniform.

So far their outfit had been lucky. Only three killed and two in hospital. Mostly the men spoke of the physical conditions in which they lived. To sustain their élan they resorted largely to kidding, but their thoughts were mostly of two things—the War and Women.

These men I shall introduce one by one.

BRAINARD

Gordon Brainard was the leader of the outfit and a fine specimen of American manhood. On leaving his university he had gone direct to the New York office of a large paper concern. Three promotions in salary and authority had given him, at twenty-six, a fairly solid place in the world.

He hadn't volunteered, feeling no obligation to fight in a European war. Conscription he had accepted stoically. He thought any decent American was willing to do his bit in a "War to End War." It would have been easy for him to get out of the ranks, but he had no military ambitions. He had been slightly wounded in the shoulder, but was soon on duty again.

In the back of his mind was the constant thought of the girl to whom he had been engaged even before he left college. The nagging thought was that if he had saved his money instead of playing bridge for high stakes, they could have been married. Gambling, not the game, had been the lure. Three or four "affairs" since coming east had left no impression on him. Carol Carlisle remained his ideal of a life companion. Through the years she had been loyal to him. He knew she was that sort—a bit old-fashioned. Now she was a nurse in a base hospital. When his company was relieved he had managed to see her. Carol would get off duty for an hour. There would be a walk, a few embraces, they would speak their love for each other, Carol always amusing and gay for both their sakes, and he would go away cursing himself for having failed her. The weary look in her eyes would haunt him. She was growing too thin though she was still lovely and moved with the old bird-like grace. He worried over her. He could have saved her from these dreadful tasks; she was never meant for such work. And so his mind ran on and on. Before sleep came he held her in his mind, hoping to dream of her.

Brainard had cast off all the religious teaching of his boyhood. Life to him was a span between birth and death. The rules were clear—to live at peace with the laws of nature and of man. A sound body, a normal mind, a fair education, a heart to love, a will to work. What more was there? What need of more? But if a bullet stopped you—well, that was that.

CUMMINGS

The handsomest of the lot in his tall, dark, romantic way was Dent Cummings. Good at soldiering, he stood up well under discipline though better educated than those he took orders from. His nerves were not steady enough for bayonet-sticking; he was nauseated and ill after it.

When conscription came he might have used his friends to get a staff position or be safely stowed in one of the home services, but he couldn't bring himself to fight for a chance that others could not have. In action he had been grazed on the thigh but was very soon back with his outfit.

Always a spectator of life, he read the unspoken thoughts of the men and listened to their racy dialogue. While they raged and cursed the dirt, the lice, the rats, the foul air and damp of the dug-outs, Cummings bore his torments silently.

Alone in life, the small income from his parents' estate, with his salary, had given him all he wanted. He had refused to enslave him-self to create a fortune. If he had a career, it was the one popularly condemned as un-American—that of a private gentleman.

No man was less effeminate, yet apparently there was no woman in his thoughts. He spoke of none, carried no photographs, and tore up most of his letters. The men marvelled at this "woman blind-ness" in a fellow who had lived in a world filled with smart and beautiful girls. Only he had the key to the mystery. He loved a woman, but she was the wife of another man, not only his friend but his employer. She was all he wanted or ever would want. Yet he hadn't spoken, fearing to disturb the peace of their home. Not that Cummings was particularly moral. Doris Fuller had helped her husband to his success as a publisher by her flair for recognizing talent; it was only decent to remain silent.

A student of history, Cummings knew what had led to the war and what would end it. The most he felt was the pity of it.

FLANAGAN

A small but wiry chap, Flanagan was a demon in close combat; he seemed to go berserk. The others wondered how a clerk in a chain drug store got that way. Like most of the A.E.F., after landing in Europe he got a feeling of inferiority. Back home everyone had praised them and thought they were good soldiers. The seasoned French fighters were quite different; but the Americans meant to show the Allies that they could make good. This edge soon wore off and left them with only the dogged determination to finish the job and go home. So with Flanagan.

He thought the war had made a "hell of a mess" of his life. Not that he liked his job or thought it much of a one. Still, he had looked forward to marrying a girl who was fine and decent, and together they could have a home, if she worked too. He paid no attention to the "floozies" who came into the store and tried to flirt with him. Then Molly Burke came along. She would have her luncheon at the soda fountain and then come to his counter for her cigarettes. That began it. They waited a year before they planned to marry. He'd go over it in his mind again and again. As soon as he was in the dugout his mind would revert to the store and Molly. It seemed some sort of protection against the nightmare he was living. He recalled the Sunday walks with Molly, evenings at the pictures, and Sunday excursions on the boats around New York. And that Sunday at the Cathedral when Molly was so sweet and devout that it strengthened his old boyhood faith. Then Molly's dancing. She was a grand little dancer. He must, when he got back, try to improve his own dancing. No use getting stodgy at twenty-six, he would say to himself.

Flanagan did not mix with the others; he had no buddy. He never seemed to smile except over a letter from his girl, the men remarked. Flanagan seldom drank except before going into action or after a bad day of it. In the outfit the little chap was respected, though he never made a confidant of one of them.

His nerves were bad and he knew it. Sleep was his only relaxation and distraction. He would lie in the dugout and, with his rosary under his blankets, pray, trying in that way to lift the strain on his taut nerves.

HANSON

The oldest and tallest of them, this Swedish-American hulk of a man was the pest of the outfit—a liar, a braggart, a bully, too, when he could get away with it. He'd been a house-painter, a sailor, a stevedore, and for extended periods a hobo. He was a terrible bore to all but his buddy, little Rosenberg, who loaned him money, which he rarely returned.

To Hanson the United States was simply the place he happened to be born in. His parents had spoken little English. Politically he inclined to the radicals, though he was too lazy to master their doctrines except the one of sharing the wealth, which he heartily approved.

With no desire to shine as a warrior, he took as few chances as possible and was expert in finding shelter for his big body when in action. The worst over, he would emerge, fire until his cartridge belt was empty as if he'd been in action all the time. He was bitterly down on the war, especially the food. Clever at foraging, he was drunk whenever he could get enough alcohol to make him so.

With women, Hanson flattered himself he was to be reckoned with. Years of battered romance, two marriages, and five offspring had not dulled his ardour. Still he denounced marriage violently. Women, he declared, had spoiled his life, first by making him a target for their wiles and then unscrupulously saddling him with their babies. Women, he declaimed, had no sense of responsibility.

Hanson thought a good deal of a plan for beating the war. He finally decided on having a case of "shock." He'd watched the men with it and knew the symptoms. His idea was that then he might get to Paris and have "some orgy." He used to tell this to Rosenberg, who seemed to think his big buddy could pull it off.

ROSENBERG

The smallest of the outfit, untidy and disorderly, Rosenberg by his friendly nature won the tolerance and goodwill of them all. Like Hanson he was devoid of hypocrisy in a lack of desire to be either a hero or a martyr.

Unlike his buddy he cared nothing for alcohol. And though Hanson was his wonder and delight, Rosenberg did not share the big fellow's condemnation of marriage. Reared on the lower East Side of New York, the youngest of eight children, he knew the strength and comfort of family affection.

He sought relief from the war in his wish-dreams. Always he longed to be back at his machine pressing pants. Theoretically he was in tune with Hanson's denunciation of capitalism, though he hoped to be a capitalist himself one day, with his own shop.

His dream of dreams was of the blonde Christian mistress he hoped to have some day, a girl who would be as loving as himself. After this extended period of bliss he would find a nice Jewish girl and marry her. Her dowry might furnish the capital for his own shop with "Morris Rosenberg" lettered on the window. They would have children to be a joy to them in their old age.

His hatred of war was inherited, and wearing a uniform did not lessen it. His imagination was too vivid to give him the hot heart of a patriot. Though Rosenberg knew from experience nothing of the United States outside New York and its environs, he felt that the future of his race lay there. For Uncle Sam he entertained the warmest feelings.

POTTER

Potter was a white-collar worker who looked older than his thirty-seven years. A bookkeeping course in a business college had led to his position in a firm that later moved to New York from the small up-state city where he was born. On their slender salaries he and his sister, a school-teacher, supported their parents. Marriage and a home had been out of the question for him.

However, Potter had been in love for five years now. Gloriously! Romantically! With the most beautiful girl in the world, the greatest actress on the screen. He carried her picture always and wrote endless love letters to her. These he destroyed, for he knew her fan mail must be enormous. As religion was his escape and comfort, he was sure that in Divine Justice she would know in the hereafter that he alone of all men on Earth had been worthy of her love and in the pure land of spirit would bestow it on him.

Potter was too old for war. Underfed and sedentary, he had been nearly killed by the training camp. He wished now he'd called himself a conscientious objector and let them send him to a Federal prison. He'd been afraid to. Besides, he'd admit in his thoughts, he'd wanted to wear the uniform, march to the band, and feel that he too was admired, cheered, idolized. Then if by some miracle *she* should learn of him, she would admire him the more.

He had no stomach for hand-to-hand fighting. He should never have been put in the infantry. "Thou Shalt Not Kill" was all he thought of when in action and he always fired too high to reach a man's body. He prayed day and night to die in his sleep like a Christian. Above all, he reiterated to himself, he must not lose faith or he would lose all. He prayed for more faith,—and then death— a falling asleep—and then—to wait for *her.*

GOERTSCH

The youngest of the lot, only twenty-one, Chris Goertsch liked soldiering. It was a relief from his early morning milk route. He found it a nice change fom the lonely, deserted streets, dim halls, and tenements he served while other fellows were having fun in the city's night life.

He was without fear and felt sure that no bullet or shell could get *him*. The little hole in his sleeve he took as a sign of his charmed life. He seemed immune even to bayonet work. His officers liked him best of all the men. Goertsch obeyed orders, was always on the job and as strong as a young bull.

Brainard liked him, had even a sort of admiration for him. To Cummings he was simply so much animated meat. Rosenberg envied him his success with women, which was unprecedented in the outfit, though Rosenberg often wondered what was so wonderful about a boy who was poor and uneducated, apart from his fresh good looks and strong white teeth. Was it that he could kill and like it?

It wasn't that Goertsch was half-witted. He knew the tragedy going on around him, the constant danger, the suffering. He simply believed that he could not be hit and he did enjoy the conflict. As a pugilist he would have been a success.

It was only when he got into uniform that he woke up to the lure of women and his power over them. He faced the fact that the girls he met while in training, and here in France, were usually on the make, but he liked to dance and was glad to pay the fiddler.

CHAPTER II

✤

THE men slept. All but Flanagan, whose nerves were ragged from listening to the sibilant sounds of Potter's whispered prayers.

The shells seemed to be coming over with greater frequency. Potter was in an agony of terror. Any moment now he and the others might be ordered into action and he felt he could not face that horror again. Panic seized him. Cold sweat ran from his pores. His heart seemed a leaden weight that was sinking. The outlines of the dugout began to recede. He could not breathe. He tried to call for help, but his voice was gone. His body seemed out of his control.

The morning was a grey mist when the word came for the men to turn out. All but one were up. None was in the mood for talk. It was a time for silence and getting their nerves steady to meet the enemy's rain of steel. As usual Hanson was vocalizing his plaints.

"A hell of a breakfast! The commissary's got a damned cheek to call this coffee. I've made better in a tomato can."

"Oh, for God's sake, drink it and shut up," Flanagan barked.

Goertsch laughed. "He thinks he's a star boarder in this outfit."

Brainard was calling them to turn out. A corporal was at the entrance waiting for them. Rosenberg had gone over to Potter.

"Get up, Potter, quick. The corporal's here." He shook him, but it was dead weight and there was no response.

"Let him alone. He's through," Flanagan muttered.

Rosenberg turned white as he stared at the still figure. Flanagan was pale himself.

"Drink your coffee, Rosenberg, and get a move on."

Goertsch came over, ready to make a joke of Potter's disobedience. With a laugh he turned the seedy form on its back. His laugh died down.

"Hey fellows! Potter's croaked!"

Cummings and Brainard came over to Goertsch and the three stood looking down on what had yesterday been, in some measure, one of them. They were silent and in their hearts they were glad of his escape. Potter had never been able to pretend. But there was no time for talk. They turned away.

Hanson came up and took a look at the man he had felt the most contempt for.

"He would," was his brief comment.

Brainard reported the death and the six went to their posts in the trench.

When the men were ordered out of the trench and over the top to make a sortie on the enemy's lines, this unit was, as usual, led by Brainard; Cummings followed next and then Flanagan and Goertsch.

Hanson was always unready and had to be sharply ordered forward by his corporal. Rosenberg was always up and out before Hanson, but managed to get beside the big fellow, who gave him a feeling of greater security, though in reality it increased his danger by offering twice as effective a target.

The daylight was growing stronger, revealing the slime and churned earth that was filled with bits of steel, shattered brush and trees, fragments of shell, and macabre bits of bone and cloth that told of deadly artillery fire that had found its mark.

Other units were going forward to the right and left. The artillery fire had been directed at a small hill, but so far it had fallen short. The men were ordered to clean out the machine-gunners near the foot of the hill. They knew they must pass through their own shell fire.

The barrage laid down made the din even more hideous. The men could only press forward and hope to take the sector in front of them. There were perhaps a hundred men in the charge. This unit was in the centre, where the machine-gun fire was heaviest. They ran zigzag fashion and were soon closing the distance between them and the enemy's first-line trench. They were well dispersed; Brainard was cutting the third barrier of wire before Hanson was out of the trench, and was well over to the right of the others when he was met by a volley that riddled his body with bullets. Cummings, twenty-odd feet away, saw him fall and ran toward him involuntarily, only to be caught in a wire and tripped. As he fell he kept his gun in his hand, and was crawling toward Brainard's body when a shell burst in front of him.

Flanagan had been surging straight ahead to their right. The ground was spitting in half-circles around him as the machine-gun bullets beat into the earth. As usual he seemed oblivious of everything but his objective and he took on a savage rage, unconscious of everything but the desire to get to the enemy and kill.

Goertsch was running, then lying flat and firing at the man whose helmet was visible behind the machine-gun and sandbags of the German trench. He was grinning as though in some sort of contest in which they were all competing for a trophy.

Hanson, as usual, had saved his fire, and as he ran he looked for a crater. He had seen the shell burst and Cummings become a cloud of fragments. Rosenberg had seen it also and his knees gave way so that he fell in sheer weakness. Hanson on his right saw him fall and, thinking the little fellow had been hit but not seriously wounded, ran to him and dragged him by the arm to a shell-hole he had sighted a few feet away. As he pitched Rosenberg down into it head-first, he laughed and said:

"Here's where we'll hang out until—"

The sentence was not finished. Hanson's mouth was closed for ever. Rosenberg looked up in time to see him falling on top of him and thought Hanson had suddenly dodged a shot. For a time he lay quietly under the big fellow's back, comforted to feel he was safe and Hanson was there with him. Presently he began to ache with the weight of the heavy body on top of him, and to ease the cramp he knew he must move. He spoke but there was no reply. He managed to get his head free and looked around Hanson's shoulder; it was all bloody. Another look and he saw that he was sharing the crater with the corpse of his old protector.

This was indeed the end for him. He had borne it all so far because he had Hanson there to bear it with him. No other man would now be close to him. He must endure it all alone. And how was he to be sure that he would ever get back to his own lines?

He was now in a complete mental collapse and seemed to be dying himself. He no longer minded Hanson's weight. His eyes closed. He was out of the battle.

When Rosenberg came back to the little world in the shell-hole, his eyes opened on the face of a small German soldier who was intent upon going through Hanson's pockets. Morris shut his eyes again quickly and lay as quietly as he could though his blood was now pounding in his ears so that he wondered the little Boche didn't hear it.

Presently he heard voices talking in German and the small thin-faced soldier rose with Hanson's wallet in his hand which he was so intent upon that he did not glance again at the body underneath. Rosenberg could see him through his half-closed eyes as he was joined by another German soldier. They went away.

"We've been driven back," he thought.

How long could he have been lying there unconscious?

He wondered if the Germans were taking prisoners.

Where were Flanagan and Goertsch?

The firing had slackened. Now and then a shell came screaming over, but there seemed to be no more machine-gun fire. Apparently the enemy had been the more successful today.

Flanagan, as usual, had started in like a maniac and got clear to the last wire when a bullet in his right leg dropped him. He lay by the wire loading and firing and finally got the machine-gunner who had peppered them.

Though much the worse from loss of blood, he kept up his fire until the last cartridge in his belt was gone. Then he lay quietly and waited. He closed his eyes when he heard the Germans coming, and rolled over on his face.

Goertsch had been a little more successful. He had gone to the left. There the gunfire had not been so fierce. The machine guns had not been trained that far and the fighting was more desultory. Again Goertsch had been fortunate and, saving his fire, he managed to make a retreat, running and loading as he ran, turning and firing again until he had dropped three of the pursuing Germans and regained the American line.

The morning's action had been disastrous for their sector. Flanagan, left for dead on the field by the Germans, after a time was able to give himself first aid and drag his body along in the mud and slime. He was weak from the loss of blood; nevertheless he managed to make the American trench lines. He did not know that the enemy was occupying them until he saw a German helmet moving behind the sandbags. He was weak and tortured with thirst. Whether he was to be killed or taken prisoner was now the question.

What did it matter? He had been a man that morning and done his duty. This is what he had got for it. Why should Potter have all the luck?

What had become of Goertsch and Rosenberg and that big stiff Hanson? Perhaps they were like Cummings now, a part of the debris.

These were Flanagan's thoughts as he lay in his face in the slime and waited for the finish.

CHAPTER III

❖

When Brainard fell with his body riddled by a German machine gun, he had no feeling of the impact of the bullets. He was, for a moment, unconscious. When he was again awake to his surroundings, he found himself standing beside his fallen body and with him was Cummings. Both were unaware of the shell that had blown Dent's body to bits.

They gazed at each other in amazement.

Where were they?

They looked about them and saw that they were exactly where they had been when Brainard fell and Cummings had tried to reach him. The guns were still firing and shells from the American side were screaming and tearing into the ground; one exploded in front of them at this moment. They thought they saw the pieces pass through each other's body. They seemed to be dreaming as they stared at each other in silence.

Presently they turned and looked for the others. Flanagan dropped with his wounded leg just at this moment and they saw the plucky little clerk keep loading and firing. Then they turned and saw Rosenberg, where he had fallen, and Hanson on the run catch hold of him and both disappear into a shell-hole.

Cummings and Brainard faced each other again and stared at Brainard's prostrate body lying between them. Still they were silent, each thinking he must be dreaming or that he had suddenly gone mad.

The barrage had ceased for the moment and the Germans were coming out of their trench. With no weapons how could they defend themselves?

Brainard seemed too dazed to realize this, but Cummings looked for his gun; it had disappeared. Brainard's was not two feet from him; he stooped to pick it up, but somehow he could not grasp it. His hand was utterly without a sense of touch. He decided that he must have been wounded in his right arm. He then tried to pick up the gun with his left hand, but he could get no hold of it.

Brainard was not thinking of the Germans but of what looked like himself lying at his feet.

The two men stared again at each other in wondering terror.

They had not uttered a word of their thoughts to each other when four Germans were upon them, who, to their surprise, paid no attention to them, and one seemed to Dent to pass directly through Brainard's figure. He cried:

"Look out!"

The Germans passed on the run without heeding them, and there was Brainard, standing as before, his eyes widened with terror.

Why hadn't the Germans done for them? What was happening?

Each feared to voice his own thoughts. Neither of them now believed the evidence of what his eyes beheld, but each decided that he must be wounded and dreaming.

They thought they saw other bodies to the right and left of them on the ground and against the wire, and men standing idly near them with no weapons in their hands—men who also seemed dazed and as if suffering from shock. There were a couple of German bodies too and German soldiers standing as if in a maze of wonderment.

Cummings knew there was small chance for them to escape, and with the Germans now sweeping onward they were caught between them. The only thing to do was wait and be taken prisoner.

Finally Brainard ventured to stoop and look into the face that seemed to be his own; it was drained white and the ground was moist with the flow from half a dozen wounds.

He began to weep.

He knelt, with his hand on what was himself but a few moments ago. He felt no sensation in the hand that rested on the quiet breast, but this he was oblivious of.

To think that here was the body that he had been so proud to keep in condition! The well-knit frame and rippling muscles had been admired by the other fellows when he'd shown himself the best of his class on the track. That fine skin and the flesh that had glowed with boyish enthusiasm in sport and with a man's passion in the years that came after.

Now all that joy was gone and this body that had meant Gordon Brainard was no more.

His mind ran back to the time when it had been a small child with his mother and—

He was unmanned by that thought and his frame was shaken with emotion.

Cummings came and stood beside him; he too was overcome. "Brainard!"

Brainard looked up, surprised out of his grief for a moment, for he had not been sure that Cummings was not a hallucination.

"What is it has happened to us, Brainard?"

"I don't know. I think I'm going crazy. Cummings, is this my body here?"

"Yes, old man, I saw you fall."

There was silence between them for a moment.

"Can it be, Brainard, that this is death?"

"No. I'm as much alive as I ever was."

"So am I, but I saw you go down and there you are lying just as you fell." He turned and pointed. "And look! There's Flanagan; he's wounded; they got him in the leg. The little devil's plugging away at that machine-gunner. . . . There! He's got him too!"

It was true. Flanagan had silenced that gun, and the gunner fell as they looked, but it was only a moment before they saw that gunner standing calmly by his post, though he did not fire again.

"Look there! It's Hanson!"

Cummings pointed to where Hanson was looming up about twenty yards back. He had no gun and he was looking about him with apparently no idea of where he was. Catching sight of them, he started toward them.

Brainard had pulled himself together.

It was strange that the most they could see of the battle was that small part of it that had been in their sight when they had somehow "gone out" for a few seconds. To the right and left of their own trench line there seemed to be nothing—absolutely nothing.

The feeling both men had was that their bodies were very light, with no sense of weariness or discomfort. They were not even conscious of the weight of their clothing or their accoutrement.

Their boots no longer seemed heavy with the caked mud. The men were comfortable and with such a feeling of energy that they were astonished as they realized it.

"Something's got me. My eyes are funny. I can't see any farther than just this sector." It was Cummings who spoke.

"Neither can I."

"I suppose it's some sort of shock. You can be almost anyhow with shock."

"Funny we should both get the same way. My God, Cummings, the thing that's getting me is that I can see my body there on the ground; and yet here I am standing talking to you."

"But I see it too; and I see you."

"I thought I was going nutty, but if you see it too, why, there's something to it."

Hanson came up to them now, running.

"Say, what's the idea? Is the war over? These Heinies seem to think we're harmless."

"They're doing plenty to us," Brainard muttered.

At that moment Hanson's eyes found Brainard's body.

"Holy Jesus! What's this?"

"I don't know myself." And Brainard wondered if Hanson too had a double.

"Where's Rosenberg?" Cummings asked.

"He's back there. He fell and I dragged him into a crater. I don't know, but I think he got his."

"The outfit's all shot. Flanagan's got it in the leg." Cummings said this and wondered if Goertsch had got off again.

The three were now walking back to the crater where Rosenberg had been tossed by Hanson. As they came to it, they looked down and saw the big body lying face-upward, his tunic open and his boots gone. In fact they were now dangling at the belt of a German soldier.

Hanson stared into the crater.

"What is this, anyway? Is this me talking or is that me there?"

"Hanson, we are dead." Cummings spoke.

"Dead, hell! I'm as good as I ever was." Then in a low tone to Brainard: "That boy's gone off his head."

"Cummings, do you mean that?" Brainard gasped.

"I can't see how it can be anything else."

Hanson was staring down into the crater.

"Look! There's Rosenberg under me."

Sure enough, Rosenberg was turning and twisting, trying to free himself.

"Hello, there, Morris, you little kike! Why don't you come out and be sociable?" Hanson bawled.

"Come along, Rosenberg," Brainard added.

"Perhaps he's been hit," Cummings said. "Are you wounded, Rosenberg?"

There was no answer. Rosenberg evidently hadn't heard them.

They repeated their questions. They shouted at him. He seemed not to know that they were there, but kept squirming out from under the weight of Hanson's body. They stooped and held out their hands to help him, but apparently he did not see them.

The little man peered cautiously over the edge of the crater toward the German trenches; his glance then veered until he faced the three, but he gave no sign that he knew they were there. He stared beyond them and saw the Germans making for his own sector.

Rosenberg crouched down again and, as he looked at Hanson's body lying in the shell-hole, he was quiet for a moment; then he threw his arm across it and burst into sobs.

Cummings and Brainard turned away. They heard Hanson **mut**ter:

"By God, I *am* dead. That damned little kike is the only **one** that'll miss me at that."

So he was dead, was he? Well, dying was a cinch. Nothing **to it.** He'd been in luck to have it come so quick and easy. Still it **wasn't** what he wanted. He'd like to live to be an old man, a very old **man,** with a woman to look after him and cook the things he liked **best.**

That was a good body lying down there. It had given him a **damn** good time, taken all together. There was a lot of fun in life if **you** had as fine a set-up as that. Six feet one and a half and no fat. **That** body would have been good for eighty years if it hadn't been **for** the damned war. Half his life gone; he'd been robbed of it just because Uncle Sam took a notion to get into this foreign mess.

And here was that little Jew, Morris, crying because he'd gone west. Well, that was more than any of his five children would do. Nothing like a buddy!

As for his wives, that last one would probably get **a** pension. He was worth more to her dead than alive.

He hated to leave the shell-hole. The only human being he **cared** for was there—himself.

The other two moved away; Hanson reluctantly followed them.

"Rosenberg can't see you, Hanson. We are spirits now, I suppose. We're invisible to him," Cummings said.

"I can't believe it. Surely we can get back in our bodies **somehow.** I'm not ready to give up my life like this," Brainard said doggedly.

"Oh, come now, old man, have any of the others come **back?** We've seen plenty of them go. Who ever came back?"

Cummings was beginning to piece together in his mind the **things** he had read about Astral bodies. Surely this was not another **world** such as he had sometimes imagined in his boyhood days. This was the same mortal world and this was the muck and slime that he had known for months with Flanagan there crawling along through it and Rosenberg lying in it, alive and natural. But he himself and Brainard and Hanson were now only souls.

The two others now seemed to feel that Cummings was right. They were dead and done for. Finally Hanson broke the silence:

"This is a hell of a Heaven."

Cummings half-smiled.

"You didn't think you were headed for Heaven, did you?"

"Well, then it's a hell of a Hell."

"It's hell enough. It was that when we were alive; ever since we were sent to this sector," Brainard said grimly.

"I suppose, fellows, that this is a new sort of consciousness we are in. I believe the Spiritualists and the Theosophists call it the Astral plane."

Hanson shook his head. "Whatever *that* is. God! I can't make head or tail of it."

They walked in silence toward the place where Gordon's body lay. He was on ahead and, for the moment, forgetful of the others. Carol! Oh, my God! It's too late now. He had lost her for ever.

Hanson was shaken; he was frightened as never before. His voice trembled as he said:

"Cummings, you mean to say this—this is the—the hereafter?"

"I suppose it must be. Some part of it, anyway."

"And we'll be here like this for ever?"

"I don't know."

There was silence.

Cummings dropped back. He was in better control of his thoughts than the others, but he too was feeling the sense of eternal separation from the world he knew and loved. Loved! Yes, now he knew that he had loved it.

What happiness he'd had in the beautiful things he knew in art! Yes, and in the gracious homes where he had been welcome. The marvels of skill, of science, that he had taken as a matter of course. What joy he had experienced in the great music that was one of his chief delights! The wit, humour, and charm of his friends! His books!

And there was Doris! How sweet it had been just to see her; to listen to her as she talked with such cleverness and vitality! How moving her voice was when she was weary!

And now it was all over. He was cut off for ever from all that, and here he was stationed in the dreadful fields of death.

CHAPTER IV

❖

WHEN the three men had come back to the body of Brainard, they stood looking at it, for in some way it was the one thing that bound them together. They had never had much in common except hardships.

Hanson had never been a man of the least importance to the other two. His conversation, his personal habits, and his views of life were all foreign to Brainard and Cummings, though they were sometimes amused at the tales he told of his exploits, and his manner of expressing his opinion of the war.

"What the hell is it all about?" he would say.

This summed up their own mental attitude and it was a refrain which they constantly heard. Brainard was too forthright to stand for a lot of Hanson's impositions. Cummings, on the other hand, had preferred to give up his own rights rather than contend for them. The small matters of their life in the dugout had been of first importance to the old hobo, but to Cummings the ultimate of discomfort and physical misery had been reached anyway.

Having only his physical well-being in mind, Hanson had always pre-empted the dryest spot in the dugout; also he had made it a point to sleep where he got the most air, even though he might shut out its circulation from the others. He had taken up more room with his belongings than any two of the other men. Always he had talked the loudest, for silence was a thing he could neither appreciate nor permit.

The only bond that had existed between the three was the enemy. Not the Germans, but the supreme enemy—the War.

Brainard and Cummings had kept their hatred to themselves. Hanson spoke his mind freely about it and, in a sense, they were grateful, for it somehow freed their feelings to hear him curse it.

They stood together now in the small terrain that had been their mental picture when they had been catapulted out of their bodies of flesh. They were now in a world so small that it seemed like a tiny patch in a sea of nothingness.

Brainard was the first to put into words a thought that each of them dreaded to avow.

"What is it we have come to? A bit of No Man's Land?"

"Looks like it," Cummings answered.

"Just a God-forsaken mud-hole," Hanson added.

"What are we going to do?" Brainard turned to Cummings.

"I suppose we can go back to the trench if we can get by the Germans," Cummings said.

"I'm for that," Hanson said eagerly.

They started back in silence. Rosenberg was still in his hiding-place and they could see Flanagan crawling toward the left. They wondered if he was still alive or—or like themselves. They went over to him.

Flanagan was caked in mud from head to foot as he crept along dragging his gun and his wounded leg. Within a few feet of him they called his name, but he made no response. They ran up and spoke to him. Hanson tried to prod him with his foot, but it seemed to pass through Flanagan's body. This so terrified Hanson that he screamed.

"God Almighty, what is this?"

"Can't you see he's alive? While we—we're in a different kind of body. Flanagan can't see us."

"D'ye mean we're like ghosts?"

Hanson stared from one to the other in horror at the idea of their fate, which his mind was just beginning to grasp. Cummings nodded.

They moved on in the direction of the trenches. The Germans seemed to have gone to some other part of the line, over to the right, for they saw only the part fixed in their mind as their sector, the place that they had been holding and that was most familiar to them. It was strange that they could not see any farther than twenty or thirty feet to the right and left of them.

"My eyes must have gone bad," Brainard said; "I can't make out anything on either side of us."

"Neither can I," Cummings answered.

"Damned if I know what's become of the army," Hanson growled.

They moved on until they came to their sector and climbed down. They went to their dugout, entered it, and looked around. It was just as they had left it.

"The old hole is here yet." Hanson had been the first one inside. "We might as well make ourselves at home again."

The other two went each to his accustomed place. They were not in the mood for talk. The mouldy and foul smell was gone; even the sense of dampness and cold had vanished. Hanson stood surveying the place with a half-smile as though glad to be safely underground once more.

"Whad'ya say we all take a snooze?"

"I'm glad to be where I can get a chance to think," was Cummings's reply.

Brainard was silent. He threw himself on his side along a bench as though he wished to be left alone with his thoughts. Hanson moved over toward the bunks and stretched himself out on his own. The silence was broken occasionally by the sound of a shell on its way to the enemy's lines.

Soon, however, Hanson was heard cursing and muttering to himself. Now that he had a chance to sleep his fill he couldn't drop off. At last even he was silent. The others were conning this new terror that had to be faced.

When they had seemingly been there an hour or more, a light suddenly appeared in the place. It entered the opening, moved toward the centre, and stopped; it was about as high as a man's head. Though it was a bright glow and the light white, it was unlike an electric light; there seemed to be no mechanism about it and it radiated from a centre. The effect was of a column of light, two feet wide and more than six feet in height, propelled by its own power.

Cummings stared at this apparition wondering if it was really there or if his imagination had created it.

"Brainard! Look!"

He wanted confirmation. Brainard raised his eyes and then quickly sat up.

"My God! What's that?"

"I don't know."

"It is a friend."

These words issued from the pillar of light in a man's voice, and the tone was friendly.

"You will soon be able to see into the radiation which has dazzled you for a moment."

This was nerve-racking after all they had experienced, though the voice was reassuring.

True enough, as they stared into the unearthly light, they began to discern the figure of a man within the aura; a young man like themselves except that he was not in their uniform. He wore the blue of a Union soldier in the Civil War; a youth of twenty-four or five, apparently, though the words he had spoken seemed to come from an older man, one accustomed to authority.

They were not quite able to identify the uniform. Neither of them had been particularly interested in the Civil War, though Brainard's father had loved to recount stories his own father had told him of the long and terrible struggle.

"You are surprised to meet a soldier of the Army of the Potomac here in France. You fell here. I in the Battle of the Wilderness."

They scarcely knew how to answer this apparition or whatever it might be. Cummings tried to speak but could find no words. The light around the figure seemed, to his vision, to be fading; or was it that his eyes were accommodating themselves to these radiations? The soldier grew more distinct.

"The shock of your death has been too recent for you to get your bearings. No wonder. You have had little preparation for entering this world. Perhaps if I tell you that I am a relative of one of you it may simplify things." He looked toward Brainard.

"You are named for me, Gordon."

"I—I'm—I'm named for my grandfather," stammered Brainard.

"That is what I mean. I am your father's father, Gordon Brainard."

This was said with an amused smile.

"But that isn't possible. He was nearly fifty when he died."

"Yes, but you see, here, in this realm, we are in appearance what we *think* we are. We come here conscious of our years. After a time we begin to look as we feel and the appearance of age gradually leaves us. You will soon learn that time is not so destructive to these bodies you inhabit now as when you were in your mortal frame."

Brainard was staring at him. "Yes, I see now. You are like a picture, a daguerreotype, my father has at home; taken when you were in the war."

Cummings had listened to all this in silence, trying to grasp it. Now he asked:

"But how did you know about us? That we—that we were killed?"

"We are here with our American troops. It is our part to receive the souls of those who fall. I have been with Gordon ever since his enlistment. How did we get here? Most of us came with the troop ships that brought you to France. Here, you see, in this life, we can only *be* where we can *think*. I had never been to Europe. I could not visualize France. So, like many other souls, I could only get here by staying with our men and crossing the sea with them. We are few to undertake such a task, but we are glad to give the fallen what aid we can."

All this seemed only words; they could not grasp the full meaning.

"But have you been here—here in this dugout with us all the time?" Brainard asked.

"No, I must be where the dead are and explain to them that they are still alive. That sounds pretty much like a paradox, doesn't it?"

"But where are *they*? We seem to be alone, we three." Cummings was speaking.

"They are here in the Etheric, the Astral plane. You have only been able to see what was in your mind's eye—your last strong impression of what you saw in those last moments in your mortal body."

"But where are we really?"

"We are in the Etheric correspondence to your sector. You will have much to learn before you can move from the place you have in your mind."

"What I'm thinking of is my folks. This will be terrible for my people and for—" Brainard broke off. He could not speak of Carol though she had been in his thoughts ever since he realized what had happened.

"Yes, that girl will find it hard to bear. Still, she is a strong soul. She will stand up to life."

"You know who I—" he hesitated.

"Carol Carlisle's family were my neighbours. I know the breed."

Brainard had turned away unmanned by the thought of Carol and his lost happiness. As if to give him a chance to recover himself, the man in blue now turned to Cummings with a friendly smile.

"We shall be glad to take you in charge, my young friend. You will need a little help."

Cummings felt a wave of goodwill pass between them.

"I'll be glad to learn what I can. I confess I haven't the faintest idea what life after death is like."

"That, my boy, is the crowning sin of modern life. People are given either a picture of a heaven that is a place of gold mansions, set with precious stones, and the whole population singing eternally, or the materialists' idea of total extinction. But now we must find a way of getting you boys out of here and into our camp. We shall need help."

CHAPTER V

❖

HANSON was now awake and, hearing a strange voice, he opened his eyes and turned over to see whom it belonged to. What he saw was a long column of light out of which the voice came. He had a vision of Judgment Day and, fearing his record might be under scrutiny, closed his eyes again and feigned sleep. He listened to what was said and was not a little puzzled. He was too frightened to speak or to attract attention to himself. Still he wanted somehow to get the gist of what was going on. His chief fear was that he might lose the company of his two comrades. He was wondering just what he should do, when he heard the voice say:

"Now we must find a way of getting you boys out of here."

He heard no more, his one thought was that they were leaving. He was scared at the idea of being abandoned and he felt he must remind them of his presence somehow, so he began to choke and cough. The effort, of course, caused him to sit up.

The light began to move slowly toward him. Hanson felt a creeping fear that was paralysing. A light that spoke, and moved of itself! What kind of hell was this!

"Well, my friend, you seem to have had a refreshing nap. We wondered if you would wake now or sink into a sleep of weeks and months, even years, as some souls do after they leave their mortal body."

Hanson could not answer. He only stared and began to shake with terror.

"You needn't be alarmed. Very soon your eyes will become accustomed to the strong radiations coming from me and you will see that I am a man like yourself."

This was said in such a kindly voice that Hanson began to feel that it couldn't be the Recording Angel who had arrived with a list of his sins. Like most men of his class, who pretend to believe in nothing pertaining to an after life, Hanson held to many old superstitions. He had wanted to die a reformed character, but the reformation was to be as nearly an eleventh-hour affair as possible.

The voice continued:

"We are willing to take you on, but you must learn to help yourself too. You may have to give up your will until you know how to use it properly. We have too many to care for to spend time on anyone who does not co-operate."

The tone had grown a little sterner.

Hanson was beginning to see the figure of a man within the light. A fine specimen he was, too, Hanson decided; tall and slender, but with a look of strength, and wearing a dark blue monkey jacket, fastened up to the chin with brass buttons; the long full trousers accentuated the slimness. A soldier all right, thought Hanson, but what a uniform! Black shoes too, and a dark blue cap, with a visor worn with a tilt to one side.

Sure! Now he knew; it was a soldier in the war to free the niggers! What the . . . ?

He caught himself just in time, for this queer young fellow was smiling as though he had read his thoughts.

"I am not one of the A.E.F., as you see. And yet I suppose I belong to it in one sense, I and the others I work with. We are the unseen battalion, the corps of spirits who receive your dead."

Hanson tried to get this straight in his mind, without much success.

"If it were not for us you might be bound here by your own thoughts for a century or more. Your mind could only function in the surroundings you were last in contact with."

This was beyond Hanson and he gave up the attempt to make sense of it; but Cummings and Brainard were listening and making an effort to understand. They saw plainly that what this person said was true as to their sense of location. They knew that at present they had no perception of anything but the objective of the morning, their trench, and the place they inhabited—the dugout.

Hanson was so mystified that he simply stared in wonderment.

"We shall be with you again shortly."

At that the pillar of light suddenly flashed out and with it the figure from which it had radiated.

"He's gone!" came from all three.

They looked at one another in astonishment and awe. They were silent, each concerned with trying to explain what had happened. This instantaneous disappearance seemed a confirmation of their suspicions, that the whole thing was a vision or a dream.

Cummings was the first to speak.

"Look here, am I awake, and sane? Brainard, did you see that figure surrounded by light?"

"Yes, and I thought we spoke with it too."

"Then I'm not quite balmy. I began to think that I was."

"But what's it all about?" came from Hanson.

"If we've all seen and heard the same thing, I suppose it means that we're going to be shown the secret of the ages—the truth about life after death."

"If you ask me, I'll say it's a blasted swindle. All that stuff about Heaven and Hell, and the angels and devils. Why, that fellow was just a man."

Hanson had recovered his power of speech and logic.

After a moment Brainard said:

"The thing that gets me is the way he went out."

"That was the most uncanny thing." Cummings was still staring at the spot where the figure had been. " 'We shall be with you again shortly,' and then—nothing."

"It makes you wonder if you're seeing things."

"Exactly!" Cummings went on. "That is the thing that made me think it was all hallucination. I saw the light come in from the trench; it moved through the opening and stopped in front of us. But it flashed out as if it was on an electric switch."

"What do you suppose the light is, anyway?"

"It may be what they call the aura, nimbus, but I don't know. This is not like any of the pictures I've seen of such things."

They were interrupted by a great commotion from Hanson. He was trying to battle with a great rat that had taken up its residence, for the time, on his bunk. He made all sorts of noises; he struck at it; he tried to sweep it off, but the animal seemed to be quite undisturbed. The others, watching, came over and joined in the effort to dislodge the creature, but apparently the rat was unaware that his new quarters had any other occupant than himself.

"For the love of Mike, what kind of a rat is this? Is it deaf, dumb, and blind?"

Cummings had to smile at the picture they made with their frantic gesticulations, shouts, and blows, and the utter calmness and indifference of the rat, which ordinarily would have gone scampering at the first assault.

"You see," he said, "we are non-existent to that fellow. He thinks the place is empty."

Brainard was confused.

"But we see and hear him. I hear the noises outside. How can that be?"

"That's what I want to find out. The idea that we're still alive is staggering enough."

After a pause he spoke again:

"Brainard, tell me something. Why wasn't *my* body lying out there too? By the wire. I wasn't far from you when I got it. What became of me?"

"I don't know, Cummings, I saw you coming as I cut the last wire."

Hanson's voice answered: "I'll tell you, Sport. You stopped a shell."

Cummings closed his eyes.

"That, eh."

He knew what that meant. Absolute annihilation. Yet here he was, for all he could see, as sound and perfect as ever. He turned suddenly and went to the small mirror, hung on a nail, where he had shaved the last time. He stood close to it but no image appeared on its surface; nothing but the boarded-up wall opposite. He peered into the glass, but nothing of himself was mirrored there. He was the last man to indulge in the sort of self-worship that is typical of many less favoured than he, yet that familiar reflection had been *himself—Dent Cummings.* What had become of him as he knew himself?

He had realized before this that he had lost his sense of touch, and of smell too, since the familiar stench was gone, but why couldn't he *see* himself in that mirror? His sight was not gone. He could see the others and he looked down and saw his body.

An awful thought flashed on him. Perhaps his face had been—

"Brainard!" His voice was sharp.

"Well?"

"Brainard, have I—I mean, is my face gone?"

"No. Why?"

"I look all right to you? The same as always?"

"Sure."

The relief was so great that he felt weak. A moment and he pointed to the square of quicksilver.

"Try looking in that glass."

Brainard went over to it, turned this way and that to try to catch his reflection.

"What's the matter with this thing?"

"It's us. We're not made of the stuff now that shows in a mirror, evidently. I got a scare at first. I guess it's the thing we used to hear quoted from the Bible. Who was it—Paul—who said: 'We have a natural body and a spiritual body.' Well, our spiritual bodies just won't work with material things."

Brainard was pondering this when Hanson broke in:

"I won't miss anything. Beauty isn't my line."

The thought that from now on they would never see their own heads and faces held them silent for a time. Hanson's attempt at humour fell flat. Cummings finally broke the silence:

"I wonder if our beards will grow. How do we shave?"

"That man or spirit or whatever you call him that says he's my grandfather didn't seem to need a shave."

"When do we eat? That's the big question."

"Good Lord, Hanson! Are you still thinking about food?"

"What else is there to think about?"

CHAPTER VI

❖

WHEN a little while later the light appeared again, and three other luminous pillars with it, the men at least knew what to expect. The voice they had heard before was saying:

"Here are three who have just been killed and this is their dug-out. They are all Americans."

Then, as they listened, another voice, one even richer in tone and volume, said:

"There are only four of us to transport them."

By this time the men had begun to see the figures of the beings within these radiations. Two were in a sort of robe, a long garment of a deep but brilliant blue which was apparently worn over what looked like an ordinary business suit. Each wore a cap that was something like a beret and of the same colour as their robes.

One of those who were robed seemed to be the leader and in command of the others. He looked at the men in khaki and remarked to the figure in the Civil War uniform:

"Which is your grandson?"

The Union soldier indicated Brainard:

"This is my son's son."

The two other newcomers had stopped just inside the entrance. One, like Brainard, was in the blue uniform of the Federal army of the sixties. The other wore the blue robe. This latter, seemingly a boy of not more than seventeen, was unlike the others in that he seemed of an almost unearthly beauty, and the light surrounding him was more intense than the others, though the first speaker in the blue robe radiated a much stronger light than the Civil War veterans.

The leader looked at Hanson, sitting on the side of his bunk too astonished even to rise; then he turned to Brainard and Cummings, who stood at attention.

"My young friends, we have come to take you where you can learn something of the world you are now inhabiting and what the laws are that govern it. You have not been here long enough to be able to help yourselves. You can move out onto that part of the field that you still have in your consciousness, but your power to transport yourselves would end with that. You are living, in other words, in your own mind. Your last impression of your surroundings is all you are at present able to connect with. Consequently we shall be obliged to help you."

This was said in the manner of a man who is simply fulfilling a duty and, however pleasant and friendly his tone, has neither time nor words to waste.

"As you have been told," he continued, "we are souls—Americans—who are here to aid our fallen soldiers."

The youth near the entrance then stepped forward, saying:

"I'll take this one if you will help me, Brainard."

He laid his hand on young Brainard's shoulder.

The leader spoke again.

"We shall ask you to close your eyes and relax as you would if you wished to go to sleep."

Brainard spoke up:

"But can't we know where we are being taken? I'm not wounded now, I can help myself."

"You don't understand. Of course you're not wounded now. The body you have at present is of ether, though it's a perfect appearance of yourself as you were in your mortal body. We shall take you to a camp back of your lines. It is not a base hospital, such as you have, but a creation out of ether. Of course you cannot understand this now, but it will all be explained to you later. I must add that, unless you accept this help we offer, you will simply be here in a mental vacuum indefinitely."

Cummings had begun to make some sort of meaning out of this with what his own mind had pieced together. He turned to Brainard.

"What can we lose by following these suggestions? Surely you needn't hesitate when it's one of your own family offering to help you."

Brainard was too puzzled by all this to have any concrete opinion, but he felt that Cummings was probably right.

"I'm willing to do what I'm told."

Still his tone lacked conviction.

"Trust me, my boy." It was his grandfather's voice and there was a note of real affection in it. It gave him confidence.

"I'm ready."

"Be just as relaxed as you can." It was the radiant boy who spoke. "You'd better lie down on the bench there."

Brainard did so, and as he stretched out he was aware of a strong vibration that was like a mild electric current passing over and through him. He closed his eyes and almost immediately felt a positive desire to sleep.

Cummings, watching this, was amazed and startled when suddenly the three disappeared in an instant, Brainard, his grandfather, and the youth who seemed to be in control. Cummings was too astonished to more than gasp at this. The leader spoke:

"You think you have lost your friend, but you will soon regain him. Let me introduce myself before I ask you to entrust yourself to my care. My name is Morton. I am an old soul here; yes, over three hundred years I've been here in the Etheric realm, and have therefore had a chance to learn and develop the powers that man can use in this sort of existence. I am what is known here as a Master. That means that I have learned, first, Self-Mastery, dominion over my mind, and, second, to concentrate mentally to a far greater degree than you now could deem possible. Also I am a member of the White Brotherhood, a secular order formed here for the purpose of aiding the victims of this war. We also work to end this brutal conflict and to bring world peace, if that is possible to present-day man. This robe is the uniform we have adopted in order to identify one another. That youth who has just left here with your friend is a member of the Order. He has been here since 1820 and is a powerful spirit. His name is Ransome. You are to see more of him."

Turning to the man in Union blue, he continued:

"This gentleman was a comrade of your friend's grandfather. His name is Leland. He, and many of the Civil War veterans, are glad to serve the men of your generation who are slaughtered in this most diabolical of all wars. We know your sufferings, your courage, and your hatred of the brutalizing methods you have been forced to submit to. We know how vile a thing war is at best and what it has become through the fiendish ingenuity of modern men. I say all this now to assure you that we are moved by pity and the spirit of brotherly compassion when we offer help."

The deep note of indignation and the protest in Morton's voice impressed Cummings.

So here, in this after life, men knew war for what it was!

Whatever lay before him, he knew now that he was freed from the horrible murder machine in which he had been caught up.

"Is it possible that there is a place where men are done with war?" he said.

Morton smiled sadly.

"No, there is war here also. But it is the war of mind against mind. A never ending war against ignorance, superstition, and degradation. War against the enemies of the race that you but feebly estimate in Earth life. We need recruits and we shall hope to enroll you as soon as you can muster your powers sufficiently to join our ranks."

The man in blue, Leland, spoke now:

"I'm sure this young man is made of the right stuff. I'll be glad to make him my charge, if he will let me."

"Thanks. I know now that I'm in good hands."

Cummings's voice faltered but he felt as if the impact of Morton's words had battered down the door of a prison that had shut out all logic, all common sense, and all human instinct, and now were streaming in upon him the fresh and invigorating air of reason, of right, and the glorious sense of individual manhood. Whoever and whatever these beings were, surely he could better trust himself to them than to the regimenting machine-like beings—the gods whose decrees had ordered every act of his for the past year, even to taking his life from him.

"You are wise to give us your full confidence. Leland, here, will help me transport you to our place of rest."

Morton made a gesture of command and Cummings went to the bench, lay down, closed his eyes, and relaxed his mind in the thought that he was somehow safe once more. He had scarcely done this when he felt a powerful vibratory current through his whole being. Suddenly it was superseded by the drowsy feeling of one heavy with sleep. After that—nothing.

Hanson was alone, still sitting on the side of his bunk in a state of bewilderment and fear. They had all gone and now here he was alone.

Alone!

All his life he had tried to avoid any exclusive companionship with himself. He had sought the lowest of men rather than permit himself to be forced to keep his own company.

Now here he was dead, and alone!

He began to curse Cummings and Brainard for leaving him. He was their buddy. He had died as they had and just because they were better educated, and a cut above him, they were taken care of while he was left.

Even in the hereafter there was class distinction.

That young guy in the blue uniform who was kidding about being Brainard's grandfather, why didn't he bring along somebody to help *him, Hanson?*

He swore that the whole heavenly host were probably just a lot of snobs.

What could he do for himself? Stay in this rotten hole or walk out in the trenches? He was damned if he knew.

Perhaps he'd better try calling for help. He was seriously considering this when again the luminous column was before him and a voice was saying:

"So you think we're a lot of swine and we've deserted you."

Hanson was not in the least abashed and he was no longer alarmed at the sudden appearance of this visitor; he had begun to take him for granted though he didn't feel exactly at home with a queer customer who seemed to live like the filament in an electric bulb.

"What's the idea? I'm a buck private in this here A.E.F. too. Why should I get the short end? Think I want to stay in this rotten dump by myself?"

"Easy, easy! You're wasting your time talking like that. We are here to help you and we are glad to do it, but you will have to change your attitude if you expect to go very far. I'm eager to be of service to any soldier, especially one of my grandson's comrades, but I'll have to ask you to be a little more careful and keep your antagonistic thoughts to yourself."

The tone was stern and the expression also.

No man could be quicker to trim his sails than Hanson when he saw it would pay. He began to grin as he returned the other's steadfast look of disapproval.

"Oh, I was only kiddin'. Jest makin' a bluff to see what you'd say."

"That's a bad start for you. We have no time for practical jokes here. Our work is too heavy, trying to help the dead and dying on that terrible field out there. You will do well to listen to what you are told and then obey."

"Sure, I get you." Then with a shade of self pity: "I'm all in. I've had a hell of a day; gettin' killed and then goin' on livin'. It's a mess."

"Would you like to be put to sleep for a while?"

"No, no!"

Hanson was scared.

"How'd I know I'd ever wake up? The next time I dropped off might prove fatal."

Just then a man in khaki walked into the dugout.

It was Potter.

CHAPTER VII

❖

THE momentary terror that had seized upon Potter soon passed and in that release he felt himself drifting into a quiet drowse that meant his heart was slowed down and would soon be done with beating.

He knew now that his prayer had been granted.

Hastily one thought after another passed.

His mind was on his sister and the added responsibility this would mean for her.

There would be some insurance for the old folks. That would help. He knew the pride they would feel, after the first shock; pride that he was their contribution to the cause of liberty, or whatever the righteous reason that they were dying for there in France. His mother would wear a gold star for the rest of her life. He would be a glorious memory now and of far more importance in his parents' eyes than if he had gone on in his routine of the monthly cheque to them, and his job in the office.

Yes, this was a good end.

He had no fear. He knew that he, Charles Potter, was safe in the everlasting love of his God. His position now would be changed radically from that he had been occupying, for he was one of the faithful; just as after election the ones who had been true to the party were rewarded.

He reflected upon the promises of glory; of what had been said of the Meek and of the Pure in Heart; these would be blessed. So far he had missed the blessings, but all that would be made up to him now.

He knew how it would be. He would be greeted, acclaimed, and given a place beside the Throne of the Most High, along with the others who had faithfully served. He, Charles Potter, would come into his promised inheritance.

These honours and rewards would not make him proud, or forgetful of others. He meant to use his new power only for good.

Above all he would devote himself to *her*. He would prepare a beautiful future for her there with him. He would probably have to intercede for her. He would claim her and make her his special care.

Yes, he must intercede for her. Her beauty, her talent and fame had made her the target for temptation. She was very likely not religious. She was the victim of worldly success—always a spiritual handicap—and she had the adoration of millions who saw her on the screen. But for him, probably her soul would be lost.

How little she guessed that a simple soldier, one of the many hundreds of thousands, wearing their country's uniform, was the man who in the end would be her saviour! He would not only intercede for her but ask to be appointed her guardian angel. When he should be asked by the Lord what reward he wished for his years of meek acceptance of his meagre life, illumined only by his abiding faith, he would answer:

"I ask but one reward—*this woman*."

Surely his request would be granted. Then he would be near her always. She would not know it, but he would be *there*, her lover, her divinely appointed mate. He would have to wait many years for her to come to him in Heaven, but the time would pass quickly if he could pass it in watching over her.

What joy!

The light from the pocket torch above seemed to recede and he was lifted in a strange way from his bed.

That wasn't what he wanted. He wished to lie still and just *pass*. He must pray for that.

He tried but the words would not come.

He felt too weak even to think now.

Darkness!

He was quite *out* for a moment.

And now the pocket torch was casting its glow again and he saw the men all sleeping. He could hear Hanson's snore even. Was it possible that he had only been dreaming of death?

Now here he was standing by his bunk and—

Yes—he was looking down at *himself*. He was out of his body. *He must be dead.*

There must be a mistake somewhere, for evidently he was not expected. No angel had been sent to bear him away to the celestial regions. He must make an effort and find out for himself just how to go about notifying God that he had arrived.

He looked down at his prostrate body, but he was only conscious of the emotion one might feel for a suit of clothes that had been serviceable but had grown threadbare. Surely there was an end now to the old shabbiness!

And he hoped his hair would now be more abundant.

Also that his chest would broaden.

Yes, and he would like his face to be more symmetrical. Not

quite so long nor so bony. He must be handsome for her sake.

He looked at the sleepers. Well, these poor fellows would be in the thick of it in a little while.

Flanagan was not really asleep. He was such a nervous, fidgety fellow anyway. And a Catholic! He would like to tell Flanagan now that a Protestant had power with the Almighty and got an answer to his prayers.

With this thought he walked over to Flanagan and stood over him.

"You see, *I'm* out of it and you're not."

Flanagan stirred as though he had heard, but made no other sign, pretending that he was asleep, but his body twitched. At last, as though yielding to an impulse that could no longer be held under, Flanagan jumped up, went over to the body, and stood looking down at it.

Potter smiled. "I'm dead."

As he looked down, Flanagan seemed to grow rigid with a terrifying thought and started back. Turning again, he came back and laid his hand on the narrow chest; then bent down and listened.

"It's no use, Flanagan. I'm safe; freed from that mortal dust now."

Flanagan moved as if to wake the others, then suddenly changed his mind and crept back under his blankets.

Potter was curious to see how his comrades would take his passing. He had never been close to any of them, but he had a desire to know how they would speak of him. Of course they were a worldly lot, with no religious feeling, unless it might be Flanagan, and he, of course, was a Catholic.

It was dull waiting to hear what they would say when they found his spirit had fled.

The men were up and making ready for the work before them. Hanson was uttering his usual complaints about his breakfast. Flanagan had come again to look at the body, but said nothing until Rosenberg had called out to Potter to get up. Then came Flanagan's low-spoken:

"Let him alone. He's through."

Potter laughed. What a thing to say! Through! Why he hadn't *begun*.

Rosenberg took it badly. It warmed Potter to see how badly.

Then Goertsch came and turned the body over. He looked closely, then said:

"Hey, fellows! Potter's croaked!"

What a vile thing to say! Potter thought. But he stood quietly with them as the others all came and stood beside the bunk. All were silent.

The word came ordering them out.

Now what should he do? Wait? Wait until they had all gone and then call upon the Lord to take him to the heavenly rest until he could get his bearings.

Presently two stretcher-bearers came and took that Charles Potter who for fifteen years had ridden daily in the subway, eaten at the cheap lunch places, and at night had sat in the movies watching *her*. That insignificant and unnoticed member of society was on his way to still further Earthly oblivion and the democracy that is marked by a wooden cross.

He would not follow his body. He knew the disposal to be made of it and he was not a mourner. He was free. He had been reprieved. He could now concentrate on getting in touch with the Lord Almighty. He must find a way to let Him know of the dreadful state of things on Earth. Surely God could not be aware of this war or He would stop it. Also he must tell Him how little *faith* there was at present in the world. God was all-powerful and could bring peace in the twinkling of an eye.

These thoughts occupied him for a time.

He knew that the men were ordered over the top by now and he dreaded the outcome. Too much the man of peace to wish to see the battle, he yet seemed unable to endure the solitude any longer.

He went out of the dugout and into the trench. The screaming of the shells struck his ear with sounds that seemed many times increased to this new body. Wandering down the line, he watched the charge of the men across the frightful terrain. These sights were too common to interest him now and anyway he was done with it all.

What matter who won now? All men were God's children. The Americans and English might be a little dearer to the Father, but all were one in His love.

Of course there were exceptions. Those who started the war and all who sinned against the laws laid down by the churches. It didn't quite bear thinking of. He must ask to have this business of Christians going to war cleared up.

So far as he knew, he had not killed anyone, always aiming high. *He* was free of guilt, but the rest—

No, he wouldn't attempt to think that through now.

Wandering along the trench, he had the strange experience of seeming always to be in the same place—the stretch in front of their dugout.

Finally he began to despair of concentrating on his prayers for help to take him away from Earth to Heaven.

He was making his way back to his old quarters, in the hope that his mental control would improve, when he saw a figure in blue. A strange old-fashioned uniform just ahead of him. The wearer was a young chap and seemed to be making for Potter's dugout. He must be someone like himself, a stray spirit trying to find his way.

CHAPTER VIII

❖

WHEN Potter entered the dugout, he saw Hanson sitting on the side of his bunk. That was mighty strange, for he had seen Hanson fall on the field. Now here he was, and, facing him, the young soldier in the blue Civil War uniform. He thought at first that Hanson was simply a memory; but no, he was speaking to the young soldier.

"I think you'd better take me along awake. I don't dare go to sleep in this place any more. Too many crazy things are happening."

"We can't move you while you are awake. Your mind pulls against ours," the soldier said.

By this time Hanson saw Potter coming toward him.

"Holy mackerel! There's Potter walking in on us. He didn't stay dead neither."

Brainard turned and saw Potter's puzzled face as he fixed his eyes on Hanson, who was saying:

"Say, Potter, haven't they planted you yet?"

Potter felt the same old disgust for Hanson's coarse humour though he no longer feared to speak his mind in rebuke.

"You'd better begin to think of meeting your God, Hanson, instead of trying to be funny."

Brainard now turned to Potter.

"You died in your bed instead of on the field."

"Yes. I died like a Christian."

Potter felt a surge of pride.

The soldier went on: "I suppose you mean that you have faith in immortality."

"Yes indeed! And I'm ready to follow the banner of Jesus Christ and enter into glory with Him."

Potter was quite sure of himself now that he had declared his principles.

"Well, that is very fine, but you will have to get used to living here first."

He was actually smiling. Potter felt indignant.

"Here? With that fellow Hanson?"

"Say, what's the matter with you, Potter? I'm a better man than you any day." Hanson turned to the soldier in blue. "Don't pay any attention to him. He was always a crazy nut. Got religion on the brain."

The other turned to Potter.

"My friend, we will be glad to help you, but you will have to obey orders."

Potter smiled a superior smile.

"I am not taking orders from Civil War soldiers or any other kind now."

"No?"

The soldier's tone was not harsh, but it was very emphatic.

"You are as helpless now, very nearly, as the day you were born. You'd better be sure that you know what you're talking about. We have no time to waste. I'm going to put this man to sleep and take him to Headquarters. If you wish I'll send someone for you."

Hanson had realized by now that he must make up his mind to obey instructions, and reluctantly, with a half-frightened expression, he stretched himself out on his bunk. A moment later he was apparently asleep.

Potter stood watching the man in blue, who seemed to be concentrating his thoughts on the long, prostrate figure in front of him. Suddenly they both disappeared. A flashing out of the light that seemed to surround the young soldier, and they were gone.

The dugout was more than ever a dark horror, and Potter saw that the rats were scampering over the beams and across the floor. This was too much for him and he ran shrieking into the trench.

"Hanson! Hanson!" he screamed.

Half maddened with fear he stumbled along the trench calling Hanson. Suddenly he came to a stop.

A pillar of light was directly in front of him.

Instantly he was calm. Here was the answer to his prayers. A pillar of fire! A blessed sign to light his way to bliss!

The pillar of light seemed to have a man's voice inside it, for he distinctly heard the words:

"Be very quiet, my friend, and relax."

Potter began to sob. At last he would be taken to his heavenly home by this Angel of Light.

"Be calm or we cannot move you."

How clear the voice was! He began to feel drowsy; he slid down on his knees. Never mind the mud, he would soon be clothed in robes of light. His mind slid off into a dream of his future home— one of the mansions in the heavenly city which, through all his lonely, poverty-haunted life, he had pictured in his mind.

There was a moment of oblivion and he was awake again.

Was he back in the training camp at home in the U.S.A.?

Why, here was row on row of cots, or beds, that seemed like those in camp except that these appeared to have no legs, no supports under them. Bunks resting on nothing.

On every bed was a soldier, one of the A.E.F., and there were men in blue robes passing from one to another of them.

He himself was lying on a bed, and beside him was the Pillar of Light, though now it seemed less dazzling, and within it was a blue-robed youth who was smiling at him.

"Here we are, my friend! The journey is over."

Potter was unable to reply. He felt cheated, robbed. After all his pious thoughts, his prayers, his keeping of every commandment, was this his reward? A soldier in a soldiers' hospital! This couldn't be Heaven.

Was it possible he had gone to Hell?

That thought was too much for his overwrought nerves and he began to weep.

He was now in Eternity.

CHAPTER IX

❖

THE man who had come for Dent Cummings was apparently a person in authority. Cummings had been placed on a bed, or what seemed a bed. Brainard was already lying on a similar one next him.

Men in blue robes were passing between the rows of beds, the occupants of which appeared to be all men of the A.E.F. The next man on the other side of Cummings seemed to have a badly wounded leg; he kept saying:

"What hospital is this? . . . I want my leg attended to. . . . This is a hell of a place to bring a man, dump him down and let him bleed to death." He turned to Cummings. "Who are these guys in the blue things? Where are the nurses? I want my leg seen to. Damned fine hospital this is. It's a —— fake."

"Perhaps this isn't a hospital." Cummings wasn't quite sure what it was. "We are dead, you know."

"Dead, hell! I was doing a man-to-man job with a Boche and he caught me in the leg with his bayonet. I fell and I suppose these fellows picked me up; I don't remember."

Cummings then explained what had happened to his outfit. The soldier next him grinned sceptically.

"Say, buddy, you've got fever, that's all."

It seemed to Cummings that the youth might be right; perhaps he had been dreaming. It was all too impossible as he thought it over.

He lay quietly wondering about it. Presently he saw Hanson appear, lying on a bed that the instant before had been empty space. He saw the youth who was called Leland with him. If he had dreamed all that in the dugout he must be dreaming still. He could hear the soldier beside him swearing at the neglect of his wound and threatening to report his case to Washington as soon as he was able to be up and around.

Hanson awoke and immediately sat up. He was scared when he saw the row of beds.

"What's this place? A damned stinking hospital? What's the idea, bringing me here? You said it was Headquarters."

He turned to his escort, who stood talking to another man in a blue robe and paying no further attention to his recent charge.

Hanson left his bed and started off. He had the strange feeling that he was walking on air. His legs moved away from his bed, but he neither felt nor saw any flooring! There was no sense of standing on anything, yet he moved easily enough. What kept him from falling? He became panicky and turned quickly back to his bed, threw himself upon it, and lay flat on his back, emitting a groan. Terror again possessed him. What was this place? Why, there seemed to be no walls to this hospital; it was beds, beds, nothing but beds as far as he could see and men in those blue thingummies standing around talking together or to the patients. Were they doctors, men nurses, or what? Then he suddenly saw Potter on a bed beside him.

Holy mackerel! Was he never to be rid of that poor fish? Potter was crying. This amused the big fellow.

"Hey, Potter, what's the bad news?"

The youth who had brought him to this place turned to Hanson and spoke sternly:

"You will be wise to leave that man alone."

"He's blubbering over something. He's one of my outfit."

Potter was writhing in his agony of mind and the youth went to him, placed a hand on his shoulder, and spoke a few words in a low tone that seemed to have a quieting effect.

Others, strange men, were waking. Some with a cry for help; others appeared to be in a daze; a few got up from their beds and tried to find their way out, but there seemed to be no walls or windows or doors. They milled around among the beds, helplessly groping for a place to escape.

There was one man who was evidently in charge of the place—he who was called Morton. He appeared to mount a small platform, for he was suddenly elevated a foot or so above the heads of the other blue-robed men. These latter scattered among the beds and each made his patient sit up and give attention to the figure who was about to address them.

"Boys"—the voice was clear and musical, gentle but authoritative—"you are wondering where you are and what this place is. I shall tell you, and you will do well to give attention and accept all I say to you without protest or comment."

There was a murmur from the patients. All were men in the uniform of the U.S.A.

The speaker went on: "You have come to the place that we have called Headquarters for the want of a better name. It is a hospital, not for your bodies, but for your minds."

Another murmur. Were they in an insane asylum?

"Your minds are all you brought with you here."

A few laughed at this.

"You think you have your uniforms, and side arms, your cartridge belts and your small possessions. Those are only appearances. You yourselves are an appearance. You are now souls and you are in appearance simply the impression you had of yourself when you were suddenly thrust into this plane."

"Give me a cup of coffee and I'll show you," shouted a voice.

"We have no coffee and you have now no organs to drink with."

This brought exclamations of surprise and terror.

"You do not need food or drink now. You are in your Etheric body, and all that you need to sustain you is in the ether in which you now live and move and have your being. Your bodies of flesh you left on the battlefield."

Cummings was listening with eager intensity. He began to piece together the things he had read and to understand them, in the light of the speaker's words. He had not been dreaming, all was reality.

"You have always had this Etheric body; it resided in your body of flesh and was only separated from it when your breath ceased and severed the connection. We who are taking care of you are the souls of men who are dedicated to the task of caring for you when you lose your mortal body, and of teaching you how to adjust yourself to this new life."

Groans, sobs, and curses rose in a wave. One young soldier screamed:

"Is this all we get for being killed?"

The men in uniform began to get together as if they were faced by a foe.

"Most of you have had no spiritual training and you are unable to use your minds to help yourselves. We can only help you if you place yourself in our care and trust us."

One voice—it was Potter's—cried out: "You are liars and demons. I am a child of God and you are keeping me from my Heavenly Father."

Potter had leaped from his bed with blazing eyes and his voice still choked with sobs, of anger, terror, and bitterness. Hanson's jeering laugh followed Potter's outburst.

"Silence!" The voice of the Master rang out sternly. "You are like millions of those whose stupid and bigoted ideas have made life, both on Earth and here, a wasted experience. Worse, it is a libel on the Divine Laws of Life."

Potter was not to be silenced. "I am a Christian and a follower of my Saviour. I am one of the saved."

"Put him to sleep, Ransome. He needs rest before he will listen to reason."

Two or three of the men in blue joined Ransome and, as if by the power of their combined concentrated thought, Potter's voice sank to a protesting murmur; then he dropped onto his bed and was quiet; in a moment more he seemed to be asleep.

This incident had the effect of quieting the rest and they now seemed to be mostly curious to hear the speaker. The men were of various degrees of intelligence and some of them seemed to be able to comprehend clearly what was being said to them. Others, like Hanson, thought it all a sort of practical joke. Most of them listened in puzzled wonder.

"You are now free of pain and you are able to live without food or money-making, or the need of physical labour. You must depend upon your own mental powers for what you get out of life here. You have been through experiences that have made deep and terrible impressions. You must try to forget them."

A derisive roar greeted this.

"Yes, for your own sakes you must try to forget the horrors you have been through. We shall help you, but you must obey our instructions or you will not be able to help yourselves. You have come to the realm where all men are equal and yet where every man's status is determined by his mental powers. You will do well to rest and for a time think of what I have said. Talk among yourselves and recall, if you can, some of your early religious teachings. There is wisdom and truth in them."

CHAPTER X

✣

THE next few days were simply repetitions of the first one. The soldiers talked among themselves. They began to realize that they seemed in no need of eating or drinking anything, for they all had an extraordinary sense of vitality.

A few of the men kept dwelling on the thought of certain favourite foods until they seemed to create a semblance of them, in their own minds, and even to believe that they ate of them. This was a mental delusion though so real to them that they insisted to the others that they had fed on these fruits and dishes of which they were overfond.

The Master, Morton, explained this to them and soon the visions and the thought of food began to fade out of the minds of those who had been insisting on the reality of the choice meals they believed they had partaken of.

Morton spoke to them all *en masse* each day, explaining to the men exactly what they were as human beings. He had to begin with them as though they were children. The more educated minds had to accept the pace of the dullards and the morons, for there were morons in the A.E.F.; many of them were fine physical specimens of manhood but with the mentalities of children. Military duty in the ranks requires no very great intelligence beyond the learning of certain simple rules, and even these are acquired as much through emulating a fellow soldier as by individual mental processes.

Brainard had been awakened and Cummings told him of all that had taken place while he had slept. Once or twice Brainard's grandfather had visited him for a brief time; his work was on the field receiving the souls of the fallen and the destroyed. In these short calls he told Gordon of the work of men like himself who knew from experience what war meant. He explained though that even in the fratricidal Civil War, when there were no Red Cross nurses and an ambulance system was only beginning to be organized, and when surgeons went on the field under fire and performed amputations, no such degradations had been thought of as trench life, gas, or mechanized mass murder. He told Gordon that when the youth of the U.S.A. had been conscripted for the present war, every fine soul of both the North and the South who was still on the Etheric plane, had volunteered to go to France and aid in receiving the spirits of the lads whose bodies were doomed to perish in the carnage.

Through the years since his death he had been from time to time in touch with his son's home. Often he had enjoyed visiting the house he himself had built. He knew Carol and her people. He had heard the engagement of the young people spoken of, and often wondered at their delay in marrying. He seemed to have followed Gordon's business career also.

Strangely enough, this young-looking veteran of the Civil War was quite modern in his knowledge of the present-day business and political scene. When his grandson marvelled at this, he smiled and said:

"Why not? Men are arriving all the time who tell us of current events and the trend of the times, the problems that confront the people and the government. Do you think we lose interest in our country just because we are here?"

"But where is this?"

Brainard said: "This is Etheric France, in the vicinity of the American sectors. Every place on Earth where mankind exists has its Etheric counterpart. That is, it has the souls of those who in mortal life lived in that particular place. As they must necessarily pattern their Etheric life on the only one they remember, and they wish to be near their descendants, they create communities that correspond to the Earthly one."

Cummings chimed in: "Then there is a sort of Etheric geography?"

"I suppose you might call it that. After you are here a long time you find out that you can be in whatever place your mind can strongly picture. You yourself are externalized thought. When you learn to concentrate and create sufficient thought-power, your mind, which is you, can travel with greater speed than light. You can *be* wherever you can *think*. Of course, I could only travel in my own country, for I had never been outside of it. So I, and others like me, had to come to France as the soldiers came. You had about fifty invisible fellow travellers on the troop ship you came over on."

Bit by bit the newly arrived souls began to get the principles of life as it was lived in this Never-Never Land. The more they pondered over it, the clearer it became. They saw that when they *willed* themselves to move, they *moved*. That was apparently the first demonstration of the law they were now under.

Hanson often came over to them and tried to make a joke of it all. He seemed to feel that some sort of a "job" was being put over on them and that soon the real facts would turn out to be quite different. This idea of having no food was a bitter grievance. Also to have to listen to Morton and to try to master what he told them. This was getting on his nerves.

Hanson had lived a purely animal life and when the sense organs of his body of flesh were gone—taste, smell, and touch—he found nothing to make life worth while.

"This is a hell of a place. No eats, no booze, no gambling, and no girls. What's the idea? Women die too, don't they? Where are they? I haven't seen a skirt since I came to this damned place. It's like doing time here. Only there we did have chuck and baseball."

Cummings tried to explain that his mind was all he had to amuse himself with and that this was true of them all. Why not try to learn the way of life here? There was companionship at least and the teachers had said there were many ways of enjoying life if you made the most of their instruction and learned to work with the laws that govern life here.

"Yeah? Well give me back the body I had and you can have all of this. I'll take mine just as I had it. A damned good life it was, too. Too much hard work, of course, even before the war, but I'd be glad to go right back and ride the rods, make my coffee in a tomato can on the roadside, and just enjoy life like I used to."

Hanson was typical of most of the men, though all grades were represented, socially, mentally, and morally. It was the life of the flesh they longed for.

Potter still slept. Cummings asked the teacher who had him in charge about Potter and was told that such men were among their most difficult problem cases.

"What sort of government have we now when such fantastic ideas can prevail among people who have been sufficiently educated to keep a set of books, as this man did, I understand? We have millions on this plane who mill around waiting to keep a rendezvous with a personal deity and when we try to explain to them the truths of life here, they call us devils and demons and say we are preventing them from meeting God and from receiving the rewards they were promised. These rewards, I believe, are to be mansions of precious metals set with fine jewels. These people expect to be the chosen intimates of a deity who only requires them to spend their time in singing and playing the harp, in an eternity of praise. What can we do with such people? What are the leaders thinking of to permit such literal interpretations of the Oriental Scriptures?"

Cummings knew all that was meant by this criticism.

"It keeps the poor and simple people quiet to teach them that they will be rich, idle, and specially set apart for favour, in a life to come. There is a worldly wisdom in that teaching."

"But what a materialist's heaven they picture! Everybody rich."

Morton sometimes stopped and talked with Cummings and Brainard. They represented as good specimens as any in this collection of souls whose young bodies had so recently been slain. Morton asked them to do their best with Hanson, who seemed quite incapable of either appreciating or understanding the instruction given them all.

Cummings saw in everything the working-out of law. He sensed the truth of many old maxims, of proverbs, myths, of the stories and statements made in the Christian Bible and the older and newer religions. He found confirmation in such sayings of Jesus Christ as "I and the Father are one"; and "Whoso loveth me loveth the Father"; and "Where two or three are gathered together, there am I in the midst of them"; and so on. The universality of Mind—that was it. And the "love" spoken of so frequently in the Scriptures of all time was the creative principle.

Brainard was not so quick to grasp the way of life in this realm.

His thoughts were with Carol. He might listen and understand, but his memory pulled him away from the contemplation of these lessons; and in the hours for meditating on all that they were taught, and which their teachers had set apart for concentrating on their instruction, his mind flew to the one whose image stood out above all else in his memory—Carol.

He had no very keen feeling for the life he had now entered upon. He must endure it, but it would have no thrill, no hope, no chance for joy or expression, as he had pictured his life in his Earthly future.

What an end!

CHAPTER XI

❖

WHEN the men were coming in, men who had been killed on the battlefields, Cummings would watch them to discover one who might have a clear idea of what state of being he was in. There were always one or two who had been given some preparation for life after death. These were usually men of the faith that had explained a Purgatory to them, a place where the soul remained until it had become adjusted to the new phase of existence. These men accepted quietly the instruction given them, and seemed able to grasp the lessons that were taught them. Cummings also observed that these were the men who soon left Headquarters. Where they went he did not know.

Brainard seemed to have lost his old habit of making the best of everything and had sunk into a lethargic state of mind. He paid little or no attention to anyone. When Cummings tried to rouse him, to talk over the instructions given them, or to fraternize, he would barely listen and in a surly manner would give attention to what Cummings had to say and then lapse into his former listlessness.

The most violent cases were those men who were afraid to face the fact that they had died. They made a perfect pandemonium with their curses and denunciations of the teachers and the Master, Morton. They had never been told what death really was, even those who were advanced in their education.

None had the slightest conception of what life after death was really like. Either, as with Potter, they had a religious misconception of "the promises" contained in the Bible, or they were sure that death was an end to consciousness.

Morton often scourged those in Earthly authority in colleges and schools, and the government, and even the churches, for their refusal to investigate life following bodily death, or to prepare people to go on with life after they leave their mortal bodies.

A man who could understand and appreciate that he must now depend upon his own mental powers was a rarity, although the Master made it clear that such a man could leave Headquarters and enter on a constructive life.

Cummings wondered what life could be in this realm where there was no matter, no organized business, and a body possessed of no more senses than those of sight and sound, with the animal senses of touch, of taste, and of smell absent. What could take the place of these bodily gifts that made three fourths of the joy of life on Earth?

He felt rather sure that the men who accepted this life calmly and as a natural part of their existence were in no way superior, intellectually, to the others. *They knew;* that was what gave them the advantage.

All the time, during this period, Brainard was sunk in a depression that nothing would dispel. His mind was chained to the past. He was lost in the memories of those days when he possessed happiness, the only happiness he now longed for, that of being with Carol.

Poor Carol! She must now start a new life, a different one. She must either forget him, and all she had dreamed for them as husband and wife, and seek a new love, or end her days in lonely and bitter regret. He had failed her. She would not think of it so. He knew she would exalt his memory into a sacrifice on the altar of duty; or perhaps think of him as a victim of the monster war spirit that was devouring a generation of the world's manhood.

Any way he thought of her, it all came back to his own selfishness, carelessness, and stupidity. He had been utterly unworthy of her love. He had thrown his chance for happiness away and now he was here in this world where he must stay in an eternity of negation.

What good was his business education now? What could he do with his commercial knowledge in this place? He was even sorry to be conscious at all. How much better if the whole of him had gone back to the elements, as his body had!

He felt no desire to learn the way of life on the Etheric plane, as the Master called it; it wasn't worth bothering about so far as he could understand it. What good was it to him? His grandfather was here, but he was a stranger, and always busy, bringing in the soldier dead.

All those funny old Sunday-school lessons he had learned as a child seemed so much idiotic nonsense. What a mockery when one is confronted with the life after death as it really is!

Potter had not awakened, but Hanson, as always, was in evidence. Never a victim of shyness, and with supreme confidence in his own powers, he was a great nuisance to those about him who were trying to learn the processes of life in this strange realm.

Hanson lived in the past. He managed to find a few men who were on his own mental level and enlivened them with his coarse jokes, obscenities, and stories of his great past, in which he was always getting the better of more orderly or fastidious citizens and defying authority. His little group of attentive listeners gave him the admiring homage that he craved, applauded his attitude of defiance toward law and order, and in all ways fed his vanity.

Often he would say: "This ain't much of a world we're in now, but when you come to think it over, in *some* ways it's a hell of a sight better than that old one. You can live without working. If we only had a pack of cards here, we could have a damn swell time."

So passed the hours for these recent comrades, Cummings, Brainard, and Hanson.

When Morton would address them all, the three reacted according to their different mental attitudes. Hanson paid no attention to any of it unless he saw a chance to raise a laugh among his cronies.

Brainard listened but could not detach his mind from his own thoughts sufficiently to profit by all the instructions. He did realize, however, that all depended on his own mental exertion.

Cummings was the one who began to put the ideas into practice. He made the first trial when it was dark, for day and night followed as in the old life. Apparently they were still attached to Earth, and its rotation made the darkness and the light. He wished to see if he could move beyond what seemed to be this vast hospital of souls and reach the place he knew best in France—his outfit's dugout. He had every feature of it indelibly impressed on his memory.

Morton had said whatever place we can *think*, there we can *be*, if we can summon sufficient thought-power.

After a few trials, almost fearing to succeed, he lay visualizing the dugout and, to his surprise, he felt a slight sensation, not physical but mental, and found himself standing in the dugout.

There was Goertsch on his bed, but none of the others of his outfit were there. Flanagan, of course, he knew was wounded and would be in hospital. But little Rosenberg, where was that poor chap? The bunks were filled with strange men, all but Chris Goertsch's. A wave of pity swept over him for these poor boys, so young, so vigorous, so helpless in this trap of war.

He saw his old knapsack still hanging on a scantling. What had they done with his letters, the half-dozen from Doris that he had treasured? How foolish he had been to keep them! The thought that other eyes than his should read them was sickening. He knew the foul interpretations that some of the rougher element put on everything connected with women, and Doris's sensitive expressions would be food for their gross imaginings.

He saw that some of the articles he had owned were now appropriated and in use—his shaving set, his little writing kit. Well, he owned nothing now but his mind.

He went out into the trench and watched the occasional shells bursting in the air or ploughing into the terrain. He saw the sentries. Why not try going into a German trench?

CHAPTER XII

✤

CUMMINGS strolled out on the muddy earth toward the German lines. He came to the wire entanglements and passed through them with no sense of having touched them. He was aware of them only because there were bits of torn cloth here and there caught on the wire and fluttering in the wind—a wind he could not feel.

But what freedom he felt!

His shoes, while they looked as mud-stained as ever, seemed to be free of the clogging clay. He walked as easily as though passing over a smoothly rolled tennis court, yet with no sense of touching ground. No more could he smell the dank stench of the wet soil that was compounded of the smell of explosives and bits of rotting flesh. He began to appreciate this freedom from the senses.

His mind seemed clearer than it had ever been. He was filled with such a sense of vitality that he marvelled. Was this what it meant to die, to have a feeling of life and power so much greater than when he was in his mortal body? His sight was keener also and he saw everything with a distinctness that seemed almost an exaggeration. Not that there was anything new to see. The sky, overcast by low-hanging clouds, the earth, seamed and shell-torn, the litter of bits of trees and metal, and here and there a piece of cloth, part of a cap, a bit of leather belt or cartridge-holder.

Now he could hear the voice of the German sentry as he was

relieved. He went forward and stood looking down into the enemy's trench. The men off duty would be sleeping, all of them wrapped in God-given oblivion, the only respite from the misery of their waking hours.

He clambered down into the trench and went up to the sentry. The man gave no sign; apparently he was not aware that he was no longer alone. Cummings wondered if their own section had not often held just such visitors as he.

He heard the snores of the weary men in their subterranean quarters. He even went into two or three of them and stood among the unconscious soldiers. What a pity to destroy these lads! So very young, most of them, they looked like schoolboys.

He noted the pictures on the walls. The many little souvenirs here and there. A crucifix. Next it might be the picture of a favourite actress or café singer, cut from a magazine. Perhaps a picture postcard of some town or village or lake. These men were not ashamed to show their sentimentality. They had no shyness about their feelings as Americans have; they were at least able to express their innermost feelings and symbolize them where their comrades could interpret them. Perhaps there were no Hansons here. Possibly these men were of a common mentality and background.

The dawn was approaching. Greyness was feeling its way into the trench as he stood among the sleepers. One lad awoke and with a sharp cry, almost like a small child's, sat up, looked at his sleeping comrades, and then, with a fluttering sigh that was a moan as well, huddled down in his blankets as though to shut out the creeping day.

Cummings was now facing the problem of returning to "Headquarters." Would he be able to get back as easily as he had come away? He began to realize that he had to quiet his mind, to free it of the sad and disturbing thoughts that had filled it here in this desolate hell he knew so well. He must be quiet; yet how could he be when there seemed to be more shell fire than ever? He must lie down. He was amused as he looked at his late enemies, and wondered what they would think if they knew that a Yankee doughboy was making himself at home in their quarters.

Try as he would, he could not concentrate. His mind seemed exhausted and he was unable to summon any mental power.

What if he should be separated from the souls he had left?

What would happen to him if he were never able to return? This was a terrifying thought.

He seemed to be lying on the floor of the German dugout, yet he wasn't sure. His mind became confused. He longed to get away, yet he could only reflect on the images of the things he had just seen.

Suddenly a light came into the place, a pillar of light such as he had seen on the day of his death. He could plainly see the figure within it: a tall, fair man in the uniform of a German private. He saw Cummings and stopped. For a moment he looked down at him. He was smiling, for he recognized a soul that had been straying into the lines of its one-time enemy.

When Cummings saw the smile he ventured to speak in what German he could muster, for he had spent a summer in Germany in 1912. He tried to explain his presence and said he was trying to quiet his mind so that he could get back to the place of souls he had left.

The man was amused.

"You see," he said in German, "we are all the same, living or dead."

"Yes, we seem to be."

"What is your regiment?"

Cummings told him.

"You may have to stay here until we get into action today. Then your spirit friends will be here to look after those who are killed. They will help you then."

"My God, must I go through that hell again?"

It seemed to him that he could never face it, after the calm and peace he had known at "Headquarters."

"Soon the gunfire and the action will begin. You need not wait long. Our men will meet their mark."

His smile emphasized the implication.

What could this man be to speak like that? Was he still war-minded?

That appeared to be true, for he was now calling out in a voice of stern command:

"Wake, men! Be strong and drive the Americans back today. Wake, and make this a victory for the Fatherland!"

He passed out. Cummings rose to follow him. He saw the pillar of light disappear into the next dugout. Could it be that the words of this soul could penetrate the minds of the sleeping men? If so, both the living and the dead were bent on destruction. Was there no peace anywhere?

In his own consciousness he had always known war for what it was—a primitive instinct refined to a point, and extended beyond natural bounds to the present stage, where the human had to see himself destroyed mechanically, in most cases, and with no chance to defend himself with his personal strength.

How could peace come to Earth if even souls used their single power, that of mental suggestion to the unconscious minds of sleeping men, to rouse the war spirit? For what was all this done? Who benefited in the end?

He was now in the midst of the terrain between the lines. He knew that at any time now the order to go over the top might come.

A barrage was being put over from the American side.

CHAPTER XIII

✣

FLANAGAN was glad to be in hospital. His wound was serious. He might even be lame for life, but at least he was done with soldiering.

He was in a ward where Carol Carlisle was one of the nurses. Carol had not yet learned that Gordon was among the fatalities, and as she had heard nothing, she felt he was alive and among the fortunate in these last days of fighting. She knew that Flanagan was a member of his company, but she had no idea that he had shared quarters with Gordon.

Flanagan was also ignorant of this girl's relation to Brainard. Neither he nor Brainard had ever been communicative. They were each ignorant of the other's private life. Flanagan knew only that Brainard was his superior in education and that his life had been on a higher social and business level than his own. This made the sensitive little drug clerk draw into his shell.

Now as he lay in hospital Flanagan was in a mood to think of the future. Would his lameness make him unfit for his job? His was an employment that kept him on his feet constantly. Now he might have to use a cane. Well, he would meet all that when he came to it.

At first he had been too weary to think. For days, when the fever was on, he lay in a semi-daze. When the fever was gone, the pain from his wound made him fully conscious; then he would lie and wonder about his work, and what Molly would say when he was shipped home an incomplete man. She might be a little ashamed of a lame husband—but after all he would be a hero in her eyes. All of those who were maimed fighting for their flag would be heroes.

At this point he would begin to wonder if it was his flag that he had fought for. Well, whatever it was, he would be among those who had made good, and probably Molly would be proud that her man had done his part. Plenty of the others in the A.E.F. were not so lucky; a lot of them died of their wounds and some were too disfigured even to bear thinking of.

He tried to keep his mind on his own affairs and shut out everything else. In a week he was able to sit up and write to Molly. In his letter he made light of his pain, but put it to her that she must expect a lame lover. He even spoke of going around on crutches, but that, he assured her, would be only temporary.

One day Carol stopped beside him and asked if he knew a private in his company named Gordon Brainard.

"Oh, yes, he was in my outfit. I saw him when he got his."

"You mean he is—"

She couldn't say it.

"Yes, the day I got this leg. He and two others of our outfit."

The tray in her hand that carried the remains of a patient's luncheon clattered to the floor and she stood staring at Flanagan.

"He was a friend of yours?"

Slowly the girl's brain cleared and, as if his question had just come through, she spoke with an effort.

"Yes."

Then she looked down at the tray and broken dishes, and a sound like a moan, which Flanagan was never to forget, came from her.

Another nurse was passing and, quite mistaking that sound, made a joke about the "smash-up." Flanagan wanted to say something to show his sympathy, but he could find no words.

"I didn't know—" was as far as he got.

Carol didn't even hear him. She was only conscious of one thing —that there was no Gordon in the world now.

Her own life had stopped with his. Ever since the time when he left home for the university, and they had pledged themselves to each other, she had associated all her future with his. He would finish a term, then come home for the vacation and recount his experiences, tell of his studies, sports, the parties; and always end by saying that there was no real fun away from her; and so on, from that time through his final year and the launching out on his business career. His letters had been full of her—of *them*. She had waited and at last wondered if he would ever really need her so that he would come for her.

She knew she had never been happy in those days, except in flashes, when he was home for a brief holiday in summer, or during the flying visits at Christmas time. Her faith in him had gradually gone, yet she could not give up hope. Gordon filled her life even though he left her to face the humiliation of her family's questionings at their prolonged engagement. Her friends' jesting she would combat with a witty rejoinder that would silence them.

The war had ended this cruel situation. She had been happier in this gruelling and ghastly work than she had been for years because, in their few stolen hours together, back of the terrible fighting lines on the front, she had come to know that Gordon had really claimed her. She knew all that his character lacked and all he had forced her to suffer because of it, but this only made her love the stronger.

But now—

As she stood looking at the rude flooring and into the past years she knew that life was at an end for her. Now there would be only waiting—waiting for an end to the waiting.

But this was impossible! This sudden chaos! A world without Gordon!

She felt a surge of righteous wrath. Was there a God who could permit such a thing as that Gordon should be killed?

Then her mouth twisted in a wry smile. *God permitted this war —why should she exp—*

Oh, how childish she was!

But how could she go on here now? She might get her discharge and go home. . . . No. Anything would be better than that. Besides, she was Carol Carlisle, twenty-six and a woman. She must stand up to the work she had come to do in France.

She had helped men when they were dying to believe in a future existence. Was there such a thing? Was there a Gordon Brainard in some sort of life that she had told these dying men to believe in?

She looked up and met Flanagan's eyes. They brought her back to the instant present.

She was a nurse in a base hospital in France.

CHAPTER XIV

❖

THE patient who was the centre of attention in the base hospital was Morris Rosenberg.

The little fellow had been completely unnerved by Hanson's death and that of the others of the outfit, so that he had collapsed and been taken out of action.

He had now recovered sufficiently to move about and talk to the men who were wounded. He had no great fund of wit or humour, and little to impart in the way of information, but he was cheerful, friendly, and chatty. He could find something to say and enjoyed saying it. It might be only to discuss at length the dismal weather, or to comment at length on the way he had "gone out" when his "buddy" was killed. He found much to say about the way he used to handle his friend when Hanson and he were on a little bust. He never tired of telling of the many conquests he had made in the days before conscription. When one sick soldier tired of his good-natured gabble he would find another who would listen for a time.

He was not able to lie down quietly and think or even to interest himself in looking over the stale American newspapers. He had to be listening to his own voice. The poor fellow knew he was boring his listeners, but that never seemed to stem the flow of his monologues.

Carol was one of the nurses who attended to his wants. He was ignorant of her relation to Brainard, and when he would pour out his endless chatter and speak of his outfit, he often mentioned the names of the men. One day, soon after Carol had learned from Flanagan of Gordon's death, she was mechanically going about her duties when she heard Rosenberg telling his neighbour, a wounded Irish-American doughboy, about the men he shared the dugout with.

"Well, there was two highbrows with us. You can't mix with those kind of fellows. They're like a clam. Our bunch was all right, but those two was never what you might call congenial. Brainard was a real sport when it came down to cases, but he was like a lot of those guys that's got American families, they're snobs. You know what I mean, they give you a square deal but you can't mix with 'em."

Carol had heard Gordon's name and stopped to listen to what Rosenberg was saying. She could picture Gordon listening to the endless, aimless talk of this boring little man.

Rosenberg saw her and mistook her interest. He called out:

"Hello, girlie! Can I do anything for you?"

"Yes. Come here for a moment, please."

With a little smile and a complacent air, he came close to her.

"I want to know how Gordon Brainard was killed."

She had nerved herself to hear it now. She knew she must be able to tell Gordon's people about their son's death. For herself, she'd rather not know and let her mind retain the image of him as she'd last seen him as he held her in his arms in one of those brief meetings when, with few words, he had made her know that they were meant for each other.

Rosenberg, of course, knew only that the swellest nurse in the place had made a request to talk to him; he felt rather inflated as he joined her, knowing that dozens of eyes were on them.

"Will you come for a walk outside? I think I can get off for half an hour."

"Sure thing."

He responded quickly, with a happy glow on his face. Gee, here was luck! A nurse like this falling for him and making a date.

Carol told him where to meet her and when, and he was so elated that he told several of the other men that he had "a date with a queen."

When Carol met him he began to nestle up to her and take her arm. She managed to free herself and with a voice as steady as she could make it she asked him to tell her of Gordon Brainard's death so that she could satisfy his father and mother and put their minds at rest about him.

So this was all there was in it for him! To go over the whole horrible scene. What a let-down! He supposed he'd have to do it.

He told her that he didn't see how it happened because he was so busy fighting. All he knew was that he himself was picked up and carried off the field.

"What good will it do his family to hear how he got his? It won't bring him back."

"No," Carol answered, "but it will comfort them if they know he died doing his duty."

"Oh, he did that all right. Brainard was always the first man over the top and he never stopped once he got going."

What a nuisance this pretty nurse was! Getting him out of the comfortable ward to slosh around in the mud. Mud! Mud! Would he ever see the last of it?

Carol led him back to the hospital a very subdued Morris. He even went to bed. He had a feeling that this girl hadn't looked upon him as a man; that is, she hadn't felt any attraction toward him. He wanted to make love to a woman, to be a lover. He wanted to forget there was a war. He had hoped ever since he'd been in hospital that he could make a nurse love him. When this nurse had asked him to walk with her, he felt he had "started something," but she never looked at him all the time they walked side by side. He felt insulted. She was one of those American snobs. She was as bad as Brainard and Cummings. They felt superior to other people who were born of foreign parents.

So Rosenberg lay on his cot and decided that when he got home he would be a Socialist. Americans were all either Republicans or Democrats. He would show these high-hats.

Carol's thoughts were too far away to observe Rosenberg and his mood. She would find out what she was seeking from Flanagan when his wound was better.

The days now were endless and the nights were terror until she found a sedative that sent her into a state of quietude that was half insensibility. She wished now that she had a real belief in the old ideas of Heaven that she had accepted as a child. How ridiculous they were! Gordon as an angel would be too absurd!

What a changed world it had become now! She seemed like the shell of what she had been a few days ago. She was going on with her work as before, but she seemed to be in a void. Her own world had ceased to be. There would never be a letter, a telephone, or a sudden call—"Private Brainard wishes to see you."

He was for ever beyond her now in a silence that would last eternally. One man, of all the thousands of dying men, had muted her life.

CHAPTER XV

❖

THERE was no one so peaceful in the long rows of cots as Flanagan, for he was sure he would soon be going home.

Home!

What did the word mean to him?

A small bedroom in an old house on a shabby street.

Perhaps not even that, for the room he had occupied and had become fond of, in spite of its unattractive furniture, had probably a new tenant long ago.

He thought of home as New York City. Home was the Statue of Liberty in the harbour holding her torch aloft. It was the craft in the rivers, the tugs, ferries, giant steamers, scows, and barges; all the water traffic and the busy workers on the wharves. Home was the skyline, the gone-to-seed old downtown streets, and the noisy elevated trains. Really home was all of the city, even the parks and Fifth Avenue, the giant apartment buildings and the beautiful Hudson; the bridges and subways, the newspaper stands, the taxicabs and limousines and trucks. Most of all, it was the Cathedral and his neighbourhood parish church where he had gone to confession and taken communion.

What a thing it was to be a citizen of New York!

Always he had felt a glow when he saw the men repairing the pavements or when the fire engines clanged down the streets. He had a sense of proprietary pride in it all as well as in the efficient way the traffic police managed their difficult jobs.

He belonged to the political club of his district, attended the meetings, and held opinions as to the fitness of candidates. He sometimes even talked to his fellow clerks about the need of getting this or that city reform.

Of course he had no illusion about his place in the general scheme of things. He could not command. He was a private in the ranks of the citizenry and would never be able to give orders.

Rarely he gave any serious thought to the rest of the country. He was a citizen of New York City, the hub of the world. The rest of the United States seemed but a rather straggling and unfinished background to it. He always spoke of other cities as "a burg out in the sticks."

He had been to the near-by seashore resorts and taken short journeys by trolley car into the neighbouring states, but the natives in these places seemed to him to be slightly foreign. Because of his reserve and uncommunicative manner he had never mixed with men from other localities, even those he met in camp and since coming to France.

Frequently he'd been irritated by Brainard and Cummings when they praised some other city than his own. They often criticized New York as being un-American. This would enrage him, but he never went into the matter. Those birds were college men and thought they knew it all. Anyway, they were Protestants and what they thought didn't matter in the long run. To be a New Yorker was good enough for anyone.

That was the only flaw in his sweetheart; she was born in the "sticks"; in a town called Fairview upstate. Though perhaps it was just as well to marry a country girl. They weren't so crazy about themselves, they were more normal and natural, and they knew how to manage on a little.

Flanagan lay with the visions of his city floating before him, the sense of *home* filling his heart and mind. What a day it would be when he could go down the gangplank and see Molly's eager face seeking him out! He would be limping, perhaps even be on a crutch, and she would cry in his arms. God! How could he ever wait out the time until that day?

Rosenberg had been trying to establish some sort of comradeship with him, but Flanagan had been curt and unresponsive. He didn't want to listen to Morris and he made no concealment of the fact.

Poor Rosenberg could not understand such a fellow. Flanagan, in his opinion, had always been a grouch, but now that they were here in hospital, all that was left of the outfit, why not be buddies? However, after two or three blighted conversational attempts he was sensible enough to give Flanagan a wide berth.

Whenever Flanagan felt communicative he asked for the chaplain and told him whatever he had on his mind. The chaplain listened and understood. As for the doctors, Flanagan suspected them of favouritism and was sure his leg was not getting the proper treatment. The doctors listened to his querulous remarks about the slow progress of the healing of his wound, but they were too overworked to give any attention to his implied criticisms.

The best time was when his nurse came and chatted with him. Carol was too intuitive to miss the innate manliness of this wiry little private. Besides, he had known Gordon; that alone set him apart. Then, too, Flanagan was so decent. He had a shy and rather charming way with him when he was being cared for. He might be difficult with the doctors, but with the nurses he was always considerate and seemed to wish to be as little trouble as possible. As soon as he was able to help himself in small ways, he did so.

"You're up against too big a job here," he would say to Carol.

He had not connected her inquiries about Gordon Brainard with the change he had seen in her since, but he cursed the war in his mind for its heart-breaking demand on human endurance. Fine girls, like this one, being burnt out with work.

The only pleasure he had was when Carol would slip an old copy of a New York newspaper to him. Even the advertisements delighted him.

One night, when the lights were out, as Flanagan lay making calculations on his chance of soon getting aboard a ship bound for New York, Carol came to his bedside with her pocket torch guiding her. She had brought him a warm drink of some milky substance, but before he had finished it, she sat down on the side of his bed and asked him to tell her how Gordon Brainard had met his death. Her face was in the shadow, but something in her voice was queer, he thought.

Flanagan told her that he had seen Brainard fall and immediately Cummings had rushed toward him. Then came the shell that had simply made a shower of fragments where Cummings had been. He himself had been picked up by Chris Goertsch of their outfit. He told of how Chris had carried him on his back to the trench. The Germans had driven their line back at first, but fresh troops had come up and he heard that the Germans had been pushed back to their original position. The same old thing, he commented—men killed and maimed and nothing gained for either side.

Carol sat silent in the dark and listened.

How many other women's lives were made barren here? They were never counted. It was only the loss of the fighters that was officially noted.

Flanagan was a little frightened when he finished his brief story, and there was only silence after it. When Carol realized that there was nothing more this soldier could tell her about Gordon, she thanked him and said good-night.

Flanagan with his Celtic intuition knew her secret now. How strange she was! She went on with her work just the same. She hadn't missed a day. Well, he pitied her. Brainard was a decent fellow and was always a real sport—he'd say that much for him.

He lay there thinking of Brainard, and suddenly there was Brainard beside him, speaking.

CHAPTER XVI

❖

WHEN Flanagan recovered from his surprise and shock, he saw that the appearance of Brainard was just as he had known him in life; perhaps there was a clearer look in the eyes and something that was like a light shone around the six-foot figure. He was quite aware that it was the spirit of the man he had seen fall.

His religion had prepared him for this; in it he had been taught something of the life after death. He knew also that he had always been what is called clairvoyant and clairaudient, but he had tried to ignore his extra-sensory experiences and never spoke of them to anyone.

When he could quiet his nerves and relax he began to hear what Brainard was saying.

"Flanagan! Flanagan, can't you hear me? It's Brainard. I'm not dead. My body was killed, but I'm not dead. Flanagan, I want to speak to you. Try to listen."

Flanagan feared to speak aloud, as some of the men might be awake, yet he wished to learn what Brainard had come to say.

"Flanagan, for God's sake, try to hear me."

Flanagan tried to speak in his mind—that is, mentally to formulate every word clearly as he thought it and as though he was speaking it with the clearest utterance.

"Brainard, I hear you. What is it you want?"

"Listen, Flanagan, I have a friend here, a nurse, Carol Carlisle. She and I were engaged. I want her to know that I'm alive. Do you get that?"

"Yes." And Flanagan repeated Brainard's words as he had got them.

"That's right. Will you tell her that I shall be here again to-morrow night?"

"Yes, I will."

"Thanks, old man."

Another and more luminous figure joined Brainard's, but, strangely enough, he seemed to be in an old blue Civil War uniform, not one of the A.E.F.'s or any of the Allies' uniforms. This strange person was saying:

"You see? Many people see us and hear us by mental telepathy."

"I thought all that was trickery."

"Plenty of it is. Still, all religions have originated in the revelations that have come by such means."

The two figures moved down the long ward as Flanagan watched.

What a thing to have to break to that nurse, Miss Carlisle! Would she believe him, or would she think his fever was responsible? The thermometer under his tongue could settle that.

He tried to sleep, but what he had just seen and heard kept repeating itself in his thoughts. If only that nurse would believe him, accept his story. He had to admit that he wasn't very happy over the task before him. He knew how the highbrows looked on these things. They called them silly superstitions, or auto-sugges-tion. He tried to think just how he could plan an opening to his message for the nurse that wouldn't excite her ridicule.

Brainard had seemed very sad, he thought, perhaps because of leaving his girl. Surely that must be the reason, for we are promised joy in the life to come. But probably only Catholics are the ones to be happy. Brainard, very likely, was an atheist.

When he fell asleep, he still had no very clear idea how he should make his revelation.

Carol had been awake all night. Her self-control had given way and a flood of weeping had suddenly broken through her taut nerves. She was not alone and she made an excuse to get up from her bed and leave the room she shared with other nurses and went out into the open.

She walked and wept. Then she stumbled and fell and lay as she fell on the sodden earth. She gave up all effort to master her grief. Moans and cries came from her that were like strange voices in her ear. She beat the wet ground with her hands—a madwoman for the moment. She lost all count of the hours.

Exhausted at last, she lay in the mud as mortally wounded soldiers lie on the battlefield.

After a time a hazy sense of peace came to her. She thought it must be nature's reaction to the violence of her weeping. Her mind seemed dulled, and she scarcely realized how far she had gone or where she was.

At last her brain began to clear. She got to her knees and looked at the grey light on the horizon. She must be on duty before very long. How could she have been so insane as to act like this?

Hurriedly she rose and ran toward the hospital. What if she had been seen? How could she account for her appearance? She knew the interpretation that would be put upon a nocturnal absence. Too many nurses had been found straying into the night with convalescent soldiers for her to escape the gossip that would be set going.

When she stole quietly into her quarters, she took off her wet slippers and earth-stained bathrobe and went under the shower before the rest were awake. She even managed to find a clean, dry nightgown and slip into her bed.

Soon she was called for duty. Her head seemed to be splitting and her legs almost refused to support her. Even her hands were nerveless. She felt weak and ill all over. Her voice was toneless and her eyes smarted under the swollen lids. She felt as if some inner fire had gutted her body. Nevertheless, she dressed for the day slowly and with none of that brisk efficiency that usually made her the first to be ready for the morning duties.

After she had her cup of morning coffee, some inner machinery of her body began to operate. The sense of being an empty shell left her and she was able to move with less effort. She knew that she was pale and that her eyes betrayed a night of weeping. No one would remark on that. Often a nurse would spend the night with a dying soldier, taking down his last messages to those at home, and the tired, overworked woman after the last word and breath would go crying to her quarters. Tears were no novelty here. No one would speak of her swollen eyes.

Carol's mind was slower than usual and her fingers less adept in dressing wounds that morning. Her customary words of cheer to the men were missing. When she came to Flanagan he saw at once what had been happening with her. He was keen now to give her the message that would change everything for her.

"Nurse, are you a Christian?"

Carol finished fastening the bandage she had been winding about his leg.

"I suppose so."

"Then you believe we live after death?"

Carol hesitated. Did she believe that? Really, in her heart, she didn't. What made this little fellow so inquisitive?

"I suppose I'm like most people, I'm a little doubtful."

Flanagan hesitated, then he ventured.

"We do, though."

She looked up at him.

"Do live after death?"

"Yes."

She smiled. It was the most bitter and weary smile he had ever seen on a woman's face. She seemed to be more concerned with the bandage than with his answer to her question.

He didn't know how to go on after that. She looked up and caught the troubled look in his eyes.

"What is it?"

"There's something I have to tell you. I don't know how, exactly. Perhaps you won't believe me."

"What makes you think I won't?"

"You—you'll think I'm crazy."

Carol gave him a quick, sharp look. Was this little chap going to say he loved her? That happened often to all the young nurses when these poor boys were in their care. She looked down at Flanagan's upturned face. No, it wasn't that. He was struggling with something else. Something was burdening his mind and she must help to free him of its load.

"Crazy! Not you. What's bothering you?" He didn't speak. "I'll promise not to think you're crazy. Really."

Flanagan was at a loss and yet he must keep his promise to Brainard. He looked at the men on either side of him. They were not concerned with anything but getting their breakfast and were paying no attention to either him or the nurse.

"Miss Carlisle, I want you to take what I'm going to tell you quietly."

"Of course. Why not?"

Carol wondered what in the world was coming. Was he going to confess some terrible secret—a crime perhaps?

"Well, I'm listening."

"You see, I'm what they call clairvoyant and I hear that way too. . . . Do you know what I mean?"

"Yes, I've heard about such things."

"Miss Carlisle, last night Brainard's spirit was here and spoke to me."

She stared at him and her knees began to give way. She suddenly sat down on the side of the bed without taking her eyes off his.

"Go on." Her tone was sharp.

"He asked me to tell you that he is alive though his body was killed. He said he would come again tonight."

Carol stared at him in silence. What was this soldier telling her? That Brainard's spirit had come last night. She tried to grasp this. That meant that the dead do not die, then.

A great glow seemed to mount inside her until it brought the blood to her neck and face. She was unable to speak for the pressure of this fountain of life that had suddenly surged up in her.

Flanagan watched her.

"Go on," she barely whispered.

"That was all." He paused. "You believe me?"

"I'm trying to. I wish I could."

"It's the God's truth." She made no reply to this. "You'll be sorry if you don't, and he will too."

"If I could only see him myself."

"Well, it's up to you now. I've told you, as I promised." He closed his eyes.

Carol sat there trying to take in what his few words had meant. Gordon Brainard alive! A spirit that could speak, and send her a message. What if it were true?

Then life would be a different thing, for Gordon would still be Gordon.

CHAPTER XVII

❖

THERE had been a bit of commotion when Brainard was missing at Headquarters. He had shown no special interest during the instruction periods and his grandfather had spoken to Morton about it. The thing was very unusual that a clean and sudden death should leave a soul so indifferent to the life it found itself in.

Morton had spoken to Brainard and advised him to make an effort to learn how to transport himself through concentrating on the place where he wished to be. Of course the field of such desires was a narrow one for an American doughboy in France.

Brainard had finally broken down and told his grandfather the reason for his failure to feel any interest in his present life. He did not spare himself, but was frank in confessing his selfishness and his cruel treatment of Carol during the years past. He had only come to understand how necessary she was to him when his chance to atone was past. He declared that the future without her did not interest him.

A short time after this talk, his grandfather had said:

"Would you like to see Carol again? You can if you will make an effort."

"It's the only thing I do want. But why do you ask such a question?"

"Because you **can see** her if you will wake up and learn how to use your mind."

This acted like an electric shock. He began to ask questions and to apply the instruction given him. To hold his mind on a single idea was not easy at first, but he found that the power to do so increased with practice. At first he found it exhausting and he would feel utterly incapable of speech or movement after prolonged concentration. Still he persisted, and as he did so the reaction was less drastic.

Cummings had made his first attempt and been brought back by Morton in a state of mental exhaustion; but after he had been put to sleep for a few hours, he awakened with renewed strength. He told Brainard of his experience. Then Brainard knew that the theory was correct and that in their present bodies they could go to whatever place they could visualize, and the picturing of the place, or of a person, with a high degree of concentration, would transport one instantly.

Cummings told him how he had failed in his effort to return to Headquarters and of the dead German soldier who had advised him to wait between the lines for the American spirits who would be there to receive the souls of the slaughtered. Morton had been the one to aid him to get back. Cummings declared he was now more than ever determined to learn how to become an expert as these teachers were and master the laws that governed life in this Etheric realm.

Brainard listened in amazement to the other's account of his visit to their old dugout. He hoped never to see it again himself; still, Cummings had proved that what they were told was true about the action and power of the mind here.

The time came when the elder Brainard said he would take Gordon to the base hospital. He said he had been there himself and found Carol was still on duty. He offered to take Gordon there that night after his work on the field and at Headquarters was over.

When the time came he simply asked Gordon to picture the hospital and he would do so himself. He assured Gordon they would find themselves there if there was sufficient thought-power. The result came suddenly and Gordon found himself, with his grandfather, standing in the hospital entrance which he had been seeing in his mind's eye and where he had often waited for Carol. They went into the wards, seeking her, but she was not there. Their sight was as keen as in daylight, and in their search they saw the men asleep or awake. Brainard senior spoke:

"Many of these men will soon be at Headquarters. I come, as we all do, to receive them as they leave their bodies here. . . ."

Suddenly Gordon exclaimed: "There's Flanagan! He was with our outfit. Poor chap, I saw him crawling on his stomach, wounded but still firing. I saw that after I was killed."

"He's quite an unusual man."

"Oh, no. He's just an ordinary chap. But he's like a tiger in action."

"I don't mean that. Do you see that light that seems to come from his head?"

"Why, yes, now that you speak of it."

"Well, that shows that the radio activity of certain of his head glands is much more powerful than in the ordinary mortal."

"I see. But what does that mean?"

"Probably that he has what you people call clairvoyance and clairaudience."

"Are there really such things, though?"

"Certainly. That is what makes a medium. We can speak to such people because their extra radio activity makes it possible for them to hear us. It's all a part of the science of vibration."

Brainard was keen to hear more, when to his amazement Carol passed by them; she even seemed to pass *through* them. She carried a tray and a pocket torch and made straight for Flanagan's bed.

"There's Carol now." He was so shaken with emotion that his grandfather became alarmed.

"Steady, Gordon, you must try to keep your mind firm. I don't want to have to leave you here."

In a few moments Gordon had mastered his feelings and was able to look at Carol with some calmness. How strained she looked! He moved over to her and heard Flanagan telling her of his going west. He heard the "Good night" and was ready to follow Carol when his grandfather said:

"My boy, you are fortunate. That little soldier is able to see and hear you, I'm sure. Go over and speak to him."

"But I want to go with Carol."

"Go first and try to speak to him."

Brainard went to Flanagan's bedside and spoke his name. When Flanagan answered and showed that he saw him, Gordon realized that here indeed was a god-sent opportunity to get in touch with Carol. He asked Flanagan to tell her he still lived and told him that he would come again the following night. Flanagan heard and agreed.

It was all miraculous!

They went to the entrance and stood talking, the elder Brainard explaining and discussing the use and misuse of mediumship by people in Earth life. No progress could be made, he said, until the scientists recognized that the theory of wave lengths was the key to interplane communication. He told of the comparatively recent understanding of this principle, even among the Masters. Only when men began to arrive who in Earth life had discovered the methods of using the ether waves had they correctly comprehended these things.

"Progress here depends upon progress on Earth. We apply the knowledge your experts bring to add to what we have learned, and so a science is built up."

A figure darted past them—it was Carol. She was in her dressing-gown and bed slippers. Brainard dashed after her. Carol went down a side passage and, at its end, opened a small door. Going out, she closed it softly after her, but now in the open she walked swiftly.

The two souls followed on.

"Wait for me here."

Gorden went on. The other stopped and waited.

All through those hours of Carol's agony Gordon was beside her. He saw now the depths of the love that had been given him. He saw too the despair that had taken its place.

He remained with her, speaking his own love to her unhearing ears. He tried to calm her by concentrating his thoughts. He gave up finally and stood watching her as she lay stretched face-down on the wet ground, in the very place where they had last met and been happy for a little time.

At last Carol seemed to be aware of what she was doing. She raised her head and rose to her knees. In that moment Gordon knelt facing her. He could make himself neither seen nor felt but he was sure that she had somehow merged his spirit with hers and that she must be conscious of it in her soul.

He went back with her to where his grandfather was standing outside the little door, waiting. Carol fled inside and closed it.

Gordon was determined to stay and begged to be allowed to do so. He wanted to be sure that there would be no chance of his not being able to keep his appointment with Flanagan the following night.

His grandfather said he might stay and promised to come for him. The two said good-night, and a moment after, the figure in the Civil War uniform flashed out.

Gordon was alone. He could only think of what had just passed and of the joy that Carol would feel when she learned that he was alive and that Flanagan could hear and see him too. They could talk through him. A few hours and he could prove to her that he was living, and waiting for her.

Yes, he would try to live somehow through the long years until she should join him. Perhaps then one day they would have the happiness they had missed in their Earthly lives.

He sat down on a bench in the entrance passage and was thinking of these things and of how blind and deaf he had been. All the time there had been this unseen world around him. It was all a mystery. What a fool he had been never even to try to solve it! For he knew that the hunger of his soul had always been to know its destiny.

CHAPTER XVIII

✣

WHEN Carol could find a few minutes in which to think over Flanagan's words, she began to doubt. Everyone who understood anything of psychiatry was aware of the tricks the subconscious mind can play and of how many times hallucinations occur. Evidently Flanagan's was a case in point.

She must humour him until this phase passed. She felt the recession of the glow that at first had swept her reason away. She must not lose her moorings. It was too divinely good to be true. Gordon was dead and all the Flanagans in the world could never bring him to life. As for his spirit—there was no evidence she knew of that supported the Spiritualists in their claim that their table-tippings, rappings, and other manifestations were anything more than the power of those who called upon the spirits to answer questions to which the answer already lay in their own minds. The exposure of those charlatans whose mind-reading talent masqueraded as clairvoyance and clairaudience she had heard all about. They were the most despicable of frauds, playing on the weak minds of those bereaved ones who sought comfort in their dark exploits.

She was not to be hoodwinked and she tightened her mind against the little soldier. Of course she must humour him. He was a patient and she would deal gently with his vagaries.

What a strange being he was! She had thought him one of the

most self-controlled men she had ever cared for in the hospital. He bore pain with a fortitude that she marvelled at. His words were always few and he had not been wont to speak unless he was spoken to. He made no advances of any kind to either nurses or patients. And now he had gone off on this weird tack. She made no doubt that the poor fellow was suffering from repressions and his nerves had given way.

So with these thoughts she went on with the day's work. When night came and she made her last round, she spoke to Flanagan and he whispered:

"You'd better come back in case Brainard comes. He said he would, you know."

She promised, though it meant doing with less sleep, sleep that she badly needed. But it would be best to humour the poor chap for the time.

When the lights were out she came with the warm drink to Flanagan's bed.

"You'll wait?" he asked.

"Yes."

She sat on the foot of his bed in silence for some time; then she felt Flanagan start.

"Here he is," he whispered.

She flashed her torch on Flanagan's face. He was looking up as though at someone at his bedside. Her torch showed that there was nothing there.

"Yes, I told her." This Flanagan said under his breath as if answering a question. "I told her just what you said," he repeated.

There was a pause, Flanagan's eyes were still fixed on the same space above and beside him.

"All right, I'll repeat what you say . . . yes, word for word."

Then in a low tone Flanagan began to speak in broken sentences.

"Carol, I am here, looking at you, facing you. . . . You think I'm dead—my body is dead, but I myself am alive . . . I'm here beside you."

Flanagan's eyes were now fixed near her. There was a little pause. Carol was absolutely still and silent, wondering at this strange fantasy of Flanagan's. Presently he went on:

"It's hard to believe, dear, but it's true. Flanagan is able to hear me. . . ."

There was a longer pause.

"Carol, I can prove to you that I'm living. . . . I followed you last night when you slipped out of the hospital in your dressing-gown. . . ."

Carol gasped. Surely Flanagan couldn't know of that, and yet—perhaps he might through someone else. It might be that one of the doctors or nurses had seen her after all.

Flanagan's voice went on as though repeating the words after someone:

"You didn't know it, Carol, but I was with you when you went to the place where *we* used to go. . . . You threw yourself face-down on the muddy ground and lay there crying. . . . Carol, was that for me?"

Carol was stunned. Flanagan *couldn't* know that, no one could but herself.

Flanagan went on:

"Carol, why don't you speak? I can hear you."

The voice ceased. Flanagan was silent and watching her now. She made an effort to speak, but the words would not come. Then Flanagan spoke again:

"There is no death. . . . I am in a body of some fine substance;

they call it here an Etheric body. . . . I have been thinking of you ever since I was killed. . . . Carol, listen, dear . . . don't you remember the day during my Easter holiday in my junior year at college when we went out to the lake and you had on a white dress with blue flowers on it . . . and you tore it on one of the oar-locks in the boat? . . ."

Surely Flanagan could not have read that in her mind. She had forgotten what she had worn that day, but it all came back now.

". . . Test me, Carol. Ask me anything you can think of that will prove I'm the only one that could give the answer."

Carol found voice enough to say:

"Gordon!"

Only that.

Flanagan looked at her and said:

"He's sitting there beside you now and he's got his arm around you."

Carol was now too overwhelmed to be clear in her thoughts.

"I can't realize it. I know, Flanagan, that you're telling me what you think you see and hear, but I can't believe it. It would be too wonderful."

Flanagan went on as though repeating after someone:

"Of course it's wonderful. It's the most wonderful thing in the world. . . . Listen, Carol! Flanagan doesn't know your home or what it's like. . . . Ask any question that you know I can answer."

Carol broke in:

"But, Flanagan, you could read the answer in my mind."

Flanagan was losing patience.

"I'm no mind-reader. . . . It's no use, Brainard. She'll never believe it. Why don't you let her alone?"

He stopped and then seemed to grow impatient at something he was hearing.

"What's the good of arguing with her, Brainard? She's got it all cooked up that I'm trying to put something over on her."

Carol broke in:

"No, no! I'm sure you believe it's a spirit, when it's only your subconscious mind."

"Oh, hell, let's drop it! I'm going to sleep."

He turned over on his side as if to keep his word. Apparently his visitor was not to be put off so easily, for Flanagan kept shaking his head.

"No. No, go away and let me alone. I kept my word, didn't I? You can see yourself it's no use."

Carol felt completely baffled. This was passing all she had known of the subconscious. She began to wonder if it *could* be. What if Gordon had come back in spirit form and Flanagan had been able to see and hear him! What if he had been repeating things that Gordon was actually saying to her! Many people believed such things were possible. She had never thought much of the mental balance of such people, but what if there was really something in their claims?

Gordon! What if Gordon was there and she had refused to believe! Would he ever come again?

CHAPTER XIX

A LITTLE cloud came over the peace of Rosenberg when he realized that his case was not considered serious. Here he was in clover, with plenty of food, company, and no danger. He was happy for the first time since conscription.

Of course he missed Hanson, that prince of good companions, and he was not getting anywhere with his plans for the future. Still he was content to be out of the fighting and secure in a haven of wounded and dying men where at least his life was safe and he got a little peace of mind.

His "shock" was not serious. His mind was clear and he had regained control of his nerves. He had been sure that, once out of action with shock, he would be sent home. He was never more talkative than when he spoke of home.

The idea of home to Rosenberg was the cleaning shop where he presided chattily over his pressing machine; then the glare of lights along Broadway, the picture theatres, the street crowds, jazz music, and the excitement of New York's cheap and blaring night life.

He had long ago given up the synagogue and the old neighbours, down on the lower East Side of New York, where he had gone to school and where his family had lived in a mean tenement. He had been one of several children. The only ones to live to maturity were himself and two sisters, much older than he. The sisters had married and settled on the lower East Side, where their husbands were successful as small merchants. These two men, too old for conscription, had sons too young to be enrolled as soldiers.

Rosenberg had counted on being the star of the family now. To be sent home disabled meant that he would be treated by his relatives with all the consideration that family affection could suggest. Fine dinners—talks in which he would shine as he told of the bravery of his outfit and his own part in France.

He could wear his uniform and even in the streets he would be looked upon with reverence by all good Americans for his service in France. He would take in the shows; and having travelled abroad, he would impress everyone with his accounts of his experiences. He was able to conjure up pictures of himself as the honoured guest at banquets given by the citizens, and as the focal point of all feminine eyes when he walked on the streets in his uniform.

He saw himself raised to the level of a hero.

Now here was a doctor telling him that he was as good as ever and could rejoin his regiment in another week. His mind recoiled at the mere thought of such a disastrous suggestion. To be out of action for a month and then to be sent back to be killed or maimed —that was too hard a blow.

He had a fit of hysterical fear that left him exhausted, unable to sleep, and so nauseated that he could not eat. He was really ill for two or three days. Then nature asserted her rights and he slept, ate, and was on his feet again, though tormented and possessed by the dread of being sent back to the front.

He went to Flanagan's bed one morning and told him that the doctors were not going to send him home after all, but back to the lines.

Flanagan grinned. He was not amused at the terror-stricken Morris; his grin was a sardonic one.

"Well, what did you expect?"

"I thought if a man got shell-shock he was through, but these Goddam doctors say I'm well. Can you beat it? Well! Why, my nerves is like sensitive plants. They get so bad I can't sleep. A man that don't sleep's got no right to be at the front."

That's what war is, Flanagan reflected, no mercy on anybody; but he did not voice this opinion. He only said:

"Buck up. It can't be helped, I guess."

Then Rosenberg went to pieces in a fine spasm of fear and hysteria. When the doctors saw what was the cause of the second collapse they were not very sympathetic. They had become calloused to all such cases.

Rosenberg was not very diplomatic. He could not refrain from saying that he had earned a release from fighting. Finally he took to arguing that he should be discharged on the ground that if he was forced to go into action again, he would only collapse and that would be a waste of time for everybody concerned. So he'd only be sent back again. Very likely he wouldn't be able to get well at all then.

The doctors were not concerned with any of these arguments. Their business was to mend their patients' bodies and minds to the point where the beds they occupied could be vacated for incoming victims of battle. They could make no exceptions. Rosenberg, so far as their tests showed, was able to take his place again at the front. He would be discharged by them as fit for immediate active service in the lines.

He could only lie on his bed now and picture the horror of what he had experienced before. It would be worse this time. He would be put with a strange outfit—men who would very likely be like Brainard and Cummings. No one to help him like Hanson.

At the thought of Hanson and his coarse, warm companionship and his genius for finding a protecting shelter, he began to cry. At times he was a prey to melancholy. A veritable avalanche of self-pity would sweep over his consciousness as he saw no hope of escaping from the war.

He did not leave his bed again, but lay staring at the roof above him, and when his food was given him he rejected it. The nurses reported this new phase, for this was really dangerous.

The doctors saw that here was a case that was out of their usual experience. They could not know that Rosenberg was not a man who could be bullied into feeling the animal frenzy that is needed to make a good soldier. He was a friendly soul who could not bear to maim, or to be maimed. He loved life and he would fight to keep it. He was not made of the stuff that killers are made of. They did not realize that he would be on their hands indefinitely unless they found a way to make his discharge from active service possible.

Meantime he began to show signs of breaking under the mental strain. At first the nurses had thought he was shamming, but soon they saw that the little fellow was not able to control his thoughts. He would lie and pick at his blanket and smile the vacant smile of one who no longer has control of his mind.

In fact, Rosenberg was now safely out of the war.

CHAPTER XX

❖

GORDON BRAINARD was still haunting the base hospital and making endeavours to get through to Carol. Two or three times he imagined he had made her aware of him. She was startled by a delicate sensation on her hand and the thought of Gordon instantly flashed into her mind. She could sense a presence so strongly that she looked about her as if she expected to see him. The whole incident was over in an instant and she smiled as she thought of Flanagan's wild talk and how this was probably the result of it, in her own subconscious mind.

Again one night when Carol had been impelled to go once more to the place where they used to meet, to be alone for a few moments, she had the same sensation on her hand and the feeling that Gordon was beside her. When she went to this place it was always to renew the memory of the few happy moments they had known together there. So she felt that her strange sensations were but the result of her thoughts of Gordon.

When he found that he could not make any impression of his presence on her, Gordon was in despair. He even went among the patients to see if there might be one there who, like Flanagan, could see or hear him. If only he *could* find such another and get a message through to Carol, he might convince her of his living presence.

Every day and night he watched by the beds of the sick and

wounded. He spoke to every one of the soldiers there. Not one seemed to see or hear him. He was all but giving up hope when he chanced to see one of the men writing on a pad of paper as he sat up in bed. He had heard of automatic writing and now he would see if he could do it.

The soldier was pausing between the pages, not sure what to write next. He seemed weary and made no effort to go on. His mind empty, he was making little motiveless marks on the blank sheet.

Suddenly Brainard concentrated on the man's hand as he saw this chance. He tried to control the hand with his mind and will it to form the letters and words. He began to dictate:

"This is Gordon Brainard writing. Please tell the nurse, Carol Carlisle, that I have sent her this message: I shall be with her always."

The man looked at what he had written with amazement. He even spoke to the men near by about it.

When Carol passed by on her rounds, the men all began shouting to her to come and look at the message. She was quite prepared for a joke of some sort, so when she went to their group and the sheet of paper was handed to her, she thought she would see a request for some little extra attention in the way of food or drink. She took the sheet of paper and read what was on it. She turned a little paler and her voice trembled as she asked:

"Who wrote this?"

"I did," the writer answered, and he added: "I was writing a letter home and when I stopped and just was feeling sort of tired and not noticing or thinking much of anything, my hand felt kind of prickly and began to write. I was stumped but I went on until it stopped."

The men were awed by this explanation. A voice from a near-by bed said:

"That's what they call automatic writing. The spirits do it."

Carol turned to the man, a rough-looking chap who was recovering from a wound in his shoulder. Most of the men were eager to hear more about this automatic writing, but Carol said:

"Why, you don't believe there are such things as spirits, do you?"

There were, of course, different answers to this. A few said yes and more said no. The man who had written the message said:

"I think somebody made me write that. It was either a spirit or else my hand was controlled by somebody in this place. I certainly didn't write it. I never heard that name, Gordon Brainard, in my life."

Carol spoke quickly,

"Are you sure of that?"

"I'll swear it on a stack of Bibles."

Carol was not at all impressed. She stood looking at the man and trying to find a reasonable explanation. Most women in her place would have jumped at the message for comfort. Carol was tempted for an instant, but in the next moment she conquered the weakness and made an effort to find a rational cause for those words on the paper.

She told herself that this was simply a most unusual case of thought-transference. She had been unable to banish from her mind the things Flanagan had said. Over and over again they had repeated themselves in her mind, the message Flanagan thought he was delivering from Gordon Brainard. It had been in her thought continuously, since she had been unable to cease thinking of it. It had been so terrible to hear the words in any voice but Gordon's.

What a travesty on Gordon it had seemed. Evidently this soldier's mind had received her thought. What a perfect example of telepathy!

All the time these things were going through Carol's mind Gordon was trying to impress his thought upon her. Again she felt a faint sense of Gordon's presence. She was almost sure she heard her name. When she looked up, the impression was gone and she shook her head.

"We mustn't let our superstitions run away with us."

Then she passed along, taking up her duties again.

The man who was so sure it was a spirit was not to be downed.

"She doesn't believe in spirits, but I do. I'll bet anything you like it was a spirit that wrote that. If you wanted to, you could write a lot more that way."

The idea seemed to interest the others and they encouraged the writer to keep at it. He was not very keen, since his effort had not seemed to be authentic.

Brainard had no more force and he felt that to make another attempt would be useless. He decided simply to wait there; at least he could be near Carol and that was better than complete separation.

The men began to tell of their different experiences and the things they had heard about spirits. They were nearly all of premonitions or the séances they had attended where tables tilted and rappings were heard. When they had finished they were all pretty well in the mood to see or hear anything. The one who had written the message was not very sure, by this time, how or what he had felt or experienced when his hand had written something his mind had not dictated. He was in a maze after all the things his companions had been saying, and he began to fear that he was becoming mentally unbalanced.

Some of the stories had been concerned with obsessions by evil spirits and of the terrible crimes committed when a weak mind was obsessed by a demon. He had heard stories like these before, but they had meant very little and he had even doubted that such things could be. Now here he had been moved to write by a spirit. He determined to see to it that such a thing didn't happen to him again.

Carol was more impressed than they knew. When she had an opportunity to go to her quarters and be alone there, she took the message from her pocket, opened it, and looked at the words again. The name Gordon Brainard *was* like Gordon's own signature. How could that happen? She decided to ask the man who had written it to write that name in his own hand. That would be a real test.

In her deeper self she hoped that it could be Gordon. Her training was all against harbouring such an idea. She prided herself on freedom from all superstition and wishful thinking. She was a modern in all that the word meant in the way of mental clarity in reasoning. She had been taught in a school that had turned its back on all the records of occult science and she was not able to accept any manifestation that included such things as automatic writing.

Still, she was happier.

Some power had lifted the dead weight of sorrow she had carried since the moment she learned of Gordon's death. She had been determined to bear her grief with a fortitude that would not make her less efficient in her duty or burden her fellow nurses with the knowledge of her loss. At times she had tried to imagine what life could offer her in the years to come that would help her to endure them. Love for another was out of the question. She was a one-man woman and she knew it.

Now this foolish, this mad hope, was thrilling through her soul and even her body. Her tasks seemed less fatiguing and the hours not so long. She was stirred, against her reason, by the hope that Gordon, somehow, was living and loving her.

What a difference even the very thought made!

CHAPTER XXI

✣

"A FINE place this is—a lot of guys layin' around doin' nothin' but listen to these highbrows tellin' us where we get off at."

Hanson wanted action, yet he was incapable of mastering the technique that would enable him to move away from Headquarters. When he had exhausted the fund of his reminiscenses and called upon his imagination to supplement them, his audience faded away. He was even reduced to listening to what others had to say of themselves; men who, back home, had belonged to the class of drifters like himself.

Hanson considered that there was some hitch in the scheme of things. Take his own case. He had meant to die a religious man, but he had been taken unaware and before he had time to renounce his sins. The hereafter was supposed to be either Heaven or Hell. If this place was Hell, then of course he was being punished; but here it didn't even have the features of Hell that might have made it an interesting place. There were no devils and no one that seemed to be Satan. It certainly wasn't Heaven, so what the hell was it?

This was no place for a man like himself, a man who had beaten the game all his life up to conscription. He would like to take a punch at these teachers and especially at that one they called Morton. That was the meanest thing of all—that he didn't seem to have any punching-power now. He was like smoke. He couldn't even feel anything.

Hanson had the idea at last that this was all a dream. He must be dreaming this whole crazy lot of things that seemed to be happening. He made up his mind that he was asleep in the old dugout. He decided that the thing to do, then, was to sleep it all away. So, much to the relief of those about him, he lay on his bed and went to sleep.

Others were sleeping, Potter among them, and the teachers made no effort to awaken them. The task for caring for the men who came each day from the battlefield was all that they could manage. Morton continued to hold his daily meetings for instruction.

There were soldiers who had been there long enough to come and go at will. One young officer had even been to Paris. He was able to visit the theatres and places he had known before the war. There was one man who had been a student at the Sorbonne and who now attended lectures there. Others went to the many resorts they had frequented when they had been on leave. Each brought back stories of their experiences and told of the hordes of French spirits they had seen thronging the streets of Paris.

Cummings was meantime trying his best to steady his mind so that he could generate the thought-power to come and go without help. He knew now perfectly well that he could be wherever he could think himself, but the return was the problem. The exhaustion that followed the effort to *go* made the coming back too difficult. He did not want to depend upon these overworked spirits.

Brainard's grandfather had been very kind and given him an idea of what he could accomplish if he made the proper effort. So he lay and practised holding his mind on one idea. He dared not make it a *place* again for fear of finding himself there with no way of getting back. He concentrated on phrases from books and poems, even on the lines of some song that he remembered. He found presently that these words began to appear in the space before him. This was explained by Morton.

"The ether," he told them, "is a matrix that holds all positive thought and reproduces the mental images of any definite and sustained thought-pattern."

He also explained that all sounds produced by mortals vibrate through the ether and remain for all time. The terrible reverberations of the war machines, as well as music and other sounds, were all there, and if one was sufficiently attuned to the exact vibratory rate of these sounds, they would be audible to him. He said that scientists knew this—those who had studied the theory of vibration and were now experimenting with mechanical apparatus that would soon give mortals the knowledge and use of an instrument to pick up sounds and amplify them so that all could hear them.

Morton encouraged the men to practise mental concentration by imaging some charming object such as a flower or a loved bit of art that they remembered vividly. A few of those who had been there longest had already created such things as a book, a piece of pottery they had owned, even the reproduction of a photograph of a beloved face.

The Master explained that any Etheric creation would remain perfect until some stronger thought than that which caused its existence destroyed it. As no one ever desired to wipe out beauty, most creations remained. Naturally few cared to concentrate on producing anything that was ugly or distressing.

The many men who were unequal to sustained concentration were the chief problem. The teachers said that the average soul, on finding that there is no need for exertion to obtain food or money, sinks into a state of uselessness and indolence and is of no further benefit to himself or anyone else. These people, the teachers declared, are like the masses of unthinking mortals who clog the wheels of progress on Earth.

There were many at Headquarters who had been fortunate enough to have the spiritual instruction that gave them faith in the immortality of their souls. These men, though not always cultured or even with any advanced education, seemed to grasp the idea the teachers gave them. Others, like Cummings, with every educational advantage, found that they could not accept these strange conditions on faith, but needed the scientific interpretation of them before they could even try to work with the laws governing this strange realm.

Many of the soldiers were so bitter over the loss of their bodies and so filled with rancour that they could only curse the powers that had torn them from the life they had prepared for and sent them to the slaughter. They called these men every vile and terrible name and asked for a way to avenge themselves. All they wanted was to make those who had forced them to give up their young lives suffer as they had been made to suffer.

In vain Morton and the teachers pointed out the uselessness of such an attitude, and would say: "We are not gods. We can only teach souls how to use life in this realm." These men were too filled with hate to accept such mild counsel.

What could they gain by vengeance? Morton pointed out that the most rational plan was to work intelligently for a better Earth life. He even said that was why he, and others like him, had remained on the Etheric plane and toiled for centuries, teaching and helping souls to realize their own possibilities.

He dwelt on the old conditions in this realm. It had indeed been a Hell, a Sheol, but, as on Earth, a few enlightened and unselfish souls had dedicated themselves to the task of making it a better place. Now, as they would see, the Astral, or Etheric, plane had become a place where there was order, progress, and beauty. They were not to believe in a hell or a heaven except as they created it themselves. There was a great outcry at this.

"Is it up to *us*?"

"Is there no God to make us happy?"

And Morton answered:

"Only that much of God which is in you. You are a portion of the Divine pattern of which we are all a part."

Now that they were in the spirit world, the men, most of them, had been hoping that a God, such as they had frankly or secretly believed in, would reward them for their sufferings. Then Morton would ask:

"Have men in Earth life found any such deity?"

They had to admit that they had not.

"Then why do you expect that you are automatically to be made blessed here? You create your own world here even more than on Earth. The Law of Cause and Effect governs every soul. You have a far better opportunity here because you are not forced to labour in order to subsist. This you must realize—*all that we are is the result of our thought*. You have been in mortal life many times and in Etheric life also. You are the sum total of all you have thought in those lives. Why not rise to the idea of making your present life an advance on all the others? Whether you realize it or not, you are a part of the evolution of the human race. It is for you to decide whether you will be a help or a hindrance to its march forward."

CHAPTER XXII

❖

WHEN any of the men were inclined to argue, Morton would say:

"There is no use in pitting your opinion against the Law of Life. We are giving you the tools to work with, the means by which you can made a full and progressive life for yourselves. When we tell you how to master these laws and use them, we are doing all we possibly can for you. Make the most of this, for we shall not be able to spend time with those who make no effort to help themselves. We are too few."

Some of the men often criticized the teachers and complained that they should not be forced to help themselves. The teachers countered this by asking if they understood that no teacher or master was under the least obligation to help them at all, and that they were aided out of a spirit of brotherhood and charity.

The worst of the complainers laughed at this. What sort of a "hand-out" was it? Nothing but a lot of rules.

Morton would then be asked to deal with these rebellious souls, and with some show of impatience he would do so.

"Does it ever occur to you men to wonder what would happen if we were to abandon you? I will tell you. You would be powerless to move even from the battlefield where you fell. We can, if we would, abandon this work and you. Our minds are now so under control that we can ascend to the Spiritual plane and be rid of such as you."

"The Spiritual plane!" a few voices would exclaim.

"Yes, the plane that is the one next this. A plane inhabited by those souls who have learned to use the Law in their own behalf."

"It ought to be an improvement on this one," a voice would interrupt.

"It is in many ways. But you will have a long way to go before you come to the point where you can discard your Etheric body for a finer one with which to enter the realm that we call the Spiritual plane. To do that you must leave your Etheric body just as you left your Earthly one and found yourself in the one you now have. The separation will be caused, not by shells and bullets, but by your own high-powered thought and will. Understand, men, we shall not urge you to help yourselves. You are given your chance to learn what we can teach you. If you choose ignorance and helplessness instead of knowledge and power, that is your affair and you must take the consequences. Free will is the most precious and the most dangerous of all the Laws. You cannot be forced to do anything; you can only be persuaded. The choice is yours and the result you must bear yourself."

When these stern words sank in and these men began to comprehend all they implied, some of the protestants would begin to see the wisdom of heeding the advice given them. The majority would simply laugh off Morton's warning and continue to argue and criticize.

The best of the men—those like Cummings—had been keen to learn from the first. Naturally the teachers felt a deeper interest in such men. One day the young teacher Ransome came to him and said:

"Cummings, you have a fine mind. We are always interested in discovering mentalities that are above the average in the hope that we can persuade them to study for Mastership."

"What does that mean?"

"It means becoming absolute master of your own thought-power. After you leave the world of matter, all the power that is at your command is the power generated by thought. Those who can attain to a high degree of this use of their mentality are the dominating personalities, the greatest creators and instructors in this realm we inhabit. Mastership also includes a certain standard of culture. A Master earns and receives his degree here just as in your universities."

"But do only those with higher education receive these degrees?"

"No, this is a spiritual democracy and we can give even an ignorant and illiterate man a fine education if he has the desire for it and the will to study. Your most distinguished men in the different branches of learning, when they come to this plane, are only too happy to share their knowledge and teach. Of course we have no books, charts, or writing materials. It is all done with the mind and the spoken word. Except in the study of mathematics. There the instructor will ask for help in concentrating on the figures needed for a problem and they appear on something that looks like a blackboard. This is a slow operation, but the results, we find, are as good as those your Earthly students can show. In fact for the time and money spent on education in the Earthly United States we find the result surprisingly small as compared to what is accomplished with our method."

"The thing that surprises me continually is to find how modern your minds are on this plane."

"Yes, even those of us who have been here two and even three centuries are moderns. That is because we are making contact with each generation as it comes and hearing the thoughts and customs prevalent in Earth life at the time. Some of us cling to the old-time style of costume that was the habit of our day, but we are with the stream of current thought."

"You make the idea of life on this plane seem very attractive."

Cummings was beginning to realize that there might be a future, a career for him even in this life which, so far, had looked so barren.

"You have seen nothing of our realm yet," Ransome continued. "Here we are simply trying to salvage the souls of our war dead. When peace comes we shall all return to our own country. Then you will be able to meet the members of your family who have preceded you here. You will have the advantage of their help and probably will be a guest in their homes."

"Homes? Are there such things?"

"Certainly." Ransome smiled at the question. "Do you imagine that because people die they lose all love of a place of their own?"

"But there is no matter here. How can people have homes?"

"They can construct the *image* of that home bit by bit. First a section of wall; then a window, more wall, and a door and so on until from memory they have reproduced the place they called home in mortal life."

"It all depends upon the memory, then?"

"Yes. Of course there are men of powerful imagination, architects, artists, builders, who enjoy creating new types rather than the homes they have occupied. Our great buildings, the public homes, concert halls, and lecture rooms, are designed by such men and created by mass thought."

"I should think that would make only confusion."

"Not at all, because the designer first creates his small model. Then he has each part modelled separately for all to image on a large scale. He directs the thought of the helpers by asking their concentration on one part at a time until it is all complete. Our public homes might be compared to your great hotels."

"Who lives in them?"

"Souls who arrive and have no friends to take them in charge."

"But I haven't seen any such creations here. Haven't the French got these things?"

"Of course they have. You can't see Etheric France because you're Earthbound yet. So are we at present. We must keep near the Earth in order to help you as you come. When we return to America, our Etheric America, we can show you a realm that will surprise you."

"When shall we be going back?"

"When peace comes. Until then we must keep at our post here."

"Must we stay here too?"

"Yes. You are not able to look after yourselves yet. A few of the first comers might be sent on the next ship that takes our disabled men across. Those souls who have worked and learned to handle themselves can go home."

At the word "home" Cummings felt a longing that he had not known even when he was enduring the degradations of life in the trenches. He did not long for any particular place or scene. What he wanted was to be again among his own people, to make part of the design that is American life. He had a passionate desire once more to take his place as a cell in the body of the young giant that was coming of age.

When he tried to analyse his homesickness, he was amused. He, who had loved travel above everything, who called himself a true cosmopolitan, who had often asserted that the spirit of man should recognize no national boundaries, he had no home in the personal sense, but he knew now that he had a spiritual home and that it was with those from whom he had sprung.

CHAPTER XXIII

✤

ALONG with all he was learning, Cummings began to wonder how Doris Fuller had taken the news of his death.

Would she care?

Of course he knew she would feel regret; so would Martin. But would she miss him greatly from her life? He was not sure.

Now he was indeed alone. It might be that his mother, perhaps his father too, would be waiting for him in an Etheric home such as the teachers had described. Happy as he would be in such a reunion, it would not fill his life completely.

Now he had a desire, overwhelmingly greater than he had known in life, to be a part of another being, to give himself as a lover, to dedicate himself to the beloved.

He knew that Doris was that *one*, yet he dared not allow such an idea to possess him.

He must find out more about love. Was it possible after death?

When he finally got up his courage to the point of speaking of it, Ransome smiled and said:

"You have asked a question that lies in the heart of every man above the brutes. All the cynicism of your modern world has not killed that fundamental desire for the mate. Here we know love in its perfection. Not perhaps as you think of it exactly. Here we have solved the mystery of the ages—the secret of true mating."

"That's hard to believe."

"By that I mean that we have discovered the fact, and proved it, that every soul has its perfect complement."

"How can you possibly know that?"

"Because we find that a natural law governs that as it does all life. Your own mate has exactly the same wave length and the same vibration as yourself."

Cummings looked somewhat dashed.

"This may seem to you a very mechanical solution, but we have found it is the true one."

"But you have no mechanisms here to test such a theory. How can you know who are mates?"

"Because when they are together, the aura or nimbus surrounding their bodies, the vibratory emanations of each, blend as one. We shall be able to show you men and women who, after centuries of unhappiness because of separation from their real mates, have been united here, through this fact of vibratory unison."

"How could they become separated if they were true mates?"

"In most cases, in times past, one had died early and, instead of waiting here for the mate to come, had reincarnated so that the two were lost in different generations. Never will the soul be content and at peace until it is with the other self that, coming up through countless forms and lives from the first divided cell, has been seeking a reunion with its own."

Cummings was trying to fit this idea into his own conception of love.

"You may as well accept this. It is the only answer ever found for the universal quest of the soul."

It all sounded too scientific to be satisfying and yet—

Well, he had to admit that so far everything the instructors had told him he had been able to prove in some degree. The thing to do was first to follow their advice and master life here.

Love! He would believe Ransome was right when he could see the theory demonstrated. However, deep within him he felt a great hope.

What if this should be the answer!

If it should all be as Ransome had said and mortals could only know these things, what misery they could be spared!

His mind dwelt on Doris. Was she *his* mate? If so, then she must be far from satisfied with her life; yet she and Martin were apparently happy. There was no evidence of friction between them and they seemed quite content.

What if Martin had a mate! Not Doris, but one who, like himself, was fated to find life empty and sterile, for that was the way he felt now. Then that woman too must await a true mating with Martin after death.

The idea of true mates began to take such hold on his imagination that he found himself speculating on the loves of his other friends and even acquaintances. His conclusion was that most of them were unhappy and simply going on with life, as best they could, with a shattered ideal.

But *could* it be true—this wave-length test?

It seemed entirely too simple to be plausible. He marvelled at the way Morton, Ransome, and the other instructors calmly made their amazing statements. Evidently they believed them. Why should he doubt?

Still it was all hypothetical so far as he and Doris were concerned. Perhaps they would be proved to be not mates at all. Then he must seek out the one who belonged to him, the one who might even be seeking him. And yet he could not conjure up an ideal of happiness with anyone but Doris.

Everything about Doris had such meaning for him—her voice, the way she used her hands, her smile, and the very look of her. She was not especially beautiful, neither dark nor fair, nor of a very definite type. He had often wondered what it was that made her seem to him the most lovely of all the many women he had known. She was so essentially *right*.

Her husband had never seemed to realize how innately different she was, how fine. Martin seemed to take her entirely for granted. He'd often thought that Martin had no real appreciation of the strange and moving quality of his wife. Were others moved as he had been, he wondered. It seemed incredible that they were not. He was sure no other woman would ever create in him a desire for her as he had desired this one—the one he could not even speak his love to.

One day he was lying on his bed endeavouring to hold his mind centred on a single idea. They were like prisoners, held to this place called Headquarters, which seemed like the ward of a cosmic hospital with no windows giving on an outside world. Morton had told them that this was the training quarters to learn how to use their minds and that the very monotony would help to drive them within themselves and so aid in forcing them to *think*—the most important thing for them, providing they would learn *how* to think.

For the object of concentration he had chosen a ring that Doris usually wore, a very beautiful sapphire, the only one she wore besides her wedding ring. It was a gift from Martin and had no connection with himself. He had admired it and thought the blue stone suited the tint of her skin. The sapphire was distinct in his mind and he even focused his thought on the setting. He pictured it as lying in his hand as it once had when he asked to examine it.

When he had for some time been holding his mind on the jewel, he was startled to see the ring itself lying in the palm of his hand. For a moment he scarcely believed his eyes. He asked his neighbour if he saw anything in his hand. The soldier described the ring perfectly.

"Gee, where did you find it?"

He explained that he had been thinking of a ring like this, one that belonged to a friend, when this duplicate of it appeared.

Was this what Morton had meant when he talked about creating? It must be. He wondered what he should do with it. He tried to pick it up, but he could feel nothing; it was an *appearance* as everything was here. When he had an opportunity he asked Morton about it. The Master smiled.

"You have made the first object. You can see now the possibilities of creation from the ether. Just a word of warning: Be sure that you really desire what you create. Some people find themselves embarrassed by the things they cause to appear. We are surprised that you are able to manifest your mental images so soon and so clearly. It takes years for most people."

There it lay in his hand, a lovely signet of the woman he adored.

CHAPTER XXIV

❖

MANY of the men at Headquarters passed the time singing popular songs. They were especially fond of the ones they had sung in camp at home when they were in training.

Cummings was baffled as to the method by which the vocal sounds were produced. Since the men were now only the *appearance* of what they *imaged* as their personality, they had no vocal cords, no breathing-apparatus, no organs of any kind.

Morton explained that the mind carries the memory of the sound of both speech and music, and as both are vibratory processes, the individual's mental power is able to reproduce the sounds.

"To your Etheric hearing the voices seem as strong and the sounds as loud as those in mortal life, though they would not be audible to Earthly ears. All is relative. When you hear our great choirs you will be astonished at the fine tonal effects they are able to produce. These bands of singers, of course, are made up of those who had been musicians in Earth life. They can produce any sound that they can *think*. We have the great musical artists here and they still remember the compositions they knew. These soldiers are not very musical, but they loved those simple songs and are happy in repeating them. It's true, they are only wasting their time until they settle down and learn to concentrate and help themselves to move about. Now they are as helpless as infants. The best thing for them would be to keep quiet and not use up their strength in singing. They need all their mind-power. Of course we can only advise them. Everyone is his own master on this plane. There are uncounted millions of souls in this realm who cannot move from the locality they lived and died in. These moronic minds are so weak they cannot even learn to reincarnate. Your civilization is making this class more numerous than ever. What is the government thinking of to allow these people with helpless minds to propagate? Here, even more than there, the result is a disaster for themselves and a burden on the rest of the people."

Cummings could only admit that the government was satisfied if people kept out of jail and managed to subsist by their physical labour. He thought of the surprise some of his countrymen would feel if they could hear Morton's words—those patriots who were fond of referring to "God's country" and boasting of its "progress." What good were the inventions, the machinery, and the mass production if the people were deteriorating? He longed to be in his mortal body and preach this new knowledge up and down the land. But would they listen? He knew only too well that anything that did not flatter the ego, the average man would turn a deaf ear to. Morton apparently was not hopeful of any change in the trend.

"America is the spoiled child of the present age. How different from the early days of the Republic!"

Where would it all end, Cummings wondered.

"A hundred and fifty years and the Americans are already a decadent race," Morton declared. "The greatest opportunity a people ever had to produce a race that would lead the world, and they have failed. No amount of prosperity can make up for its present lack of character."

These were terrible indictments, yet Cummings knew they were true. He had himself harboured no illusions as to the prevailing want of moral fibre that was becoming characteristic of his countrymen. The basis of it had come with the freeing of youth from all restraints and discipline. Girls and boys were left to follow their instincts at an age when they most needed guidance and guardianship. Success was the goal at any cost, and the price paid for it did not matter. But he had not, until now, had the stark realization of what the ultimate consequences would be. He saw clearly that life on this plane must be simply the result of the other.

But it mustn't go on like this. Something must be done. What could he do? How warn his people?

He asked Morton these questions. Morton was no cynic, but he answered with a bitter smile.

"Though one rose from the dead they would not believe. You will only now see the consequences of the abandonment of the old American ideals of conduct, of regard for decency, of a sense of personal honour and integrity, of a standard of life that made character the main consideration. Most of those in Earth life in the United States have accepted the fatuous idea that they are immune to the consequences of their conceptions of life. They are answered by the gangster, the free lovers of both sexes, the drug addict, the grafter, and the demagogue who barters the people's welfare for power. Soon the effect of all this lack of the old ideals will result in a class war. What follows will be chaos. Then if the people are not wholly rotted out with egotism and greed, they may be able to salvage something to make another start with. This does not mean our material civilization, but the people themselves, their souls, their minds, and that thing we call the spirit—the immortal part of every human being. Angel or demon: either is possible. Of course there are exceptions among the citizens, men and women who strive to hold to the old principles, but either they are howled down or their efforts are ignored. Children who come to us here before they are old enough to be corrupted are fortunate. They will escape."

Cummings had not thought of children, for he had seen none since coming over. But of course children died. He questioned Morton about them. In an instant all the bitterness was gone and Morton's face seemed illuminated as he spoke.

"The most perfect specimens of young manhood and womanhood are those who come as small children. They have no memory of Earth life and are perfectly at home here. They use their mental powers in the most delicate tasks, tasks beyond the powers of most of us. All are given the education to fit them for the line of work they select. And from the time of their arrival they are made to feel that they are loved. We have no "orphans" here. Love is theirs in fullest measure. Their teachers are women and men who are natural mothers and fathers, those who find happiness in training young minds. Many a child comes from a home of poverty and squalor or from one that is a place of strife and unhappiness. We see to it that they know only the beautiful side of human nature. The poorest children are usually the happiest after they come, for we are careful to surround them, as we do all children, with objects of beauty. All their lessons, games, and exercises are made as attractive as possible. We shall show you a child world that we can very well boast of."

Cummings thought long over all these things. What a failure his old world seemed! Men and women marrying and divorcing, marrying and divorcing again and even again. Seeking to satisfy their own desires and with no sense of responsibility for the children who are shifted about. Children with no real home or sense of the solidity of their family. No wonder they were cynics by the time they reached adolescence!

What a criminal waste of life it all was! The Earth ready to yield its bounty to maintain a happy race and yet men and women so blind that they only make an attempt to satisfy their love of power or greed, excitement or thrills.

He was too sensitive to think upon all these things with unconcern. What could he do to save his people now?

Nothing, of course. It was too late.

CHAPTER XXV

❖

THERE was a fine time at Headquarters when Morton said:

"Boys, you will be sailing for home soon."

The men sent up a shout of joy. They seemed to feel that "home" would mean taking up life as it was before they had been killed.

Cummings was equally elated. He could now see the Etheric U.S.A. He longed to be again among familiar scenes and where he could find his own way about. Of course he was hoping to meet his parents, who had passed years ago into this realm. There were friends also, more recent arrivals.

He wondered too if he could see Doris Fuller. Would it be wise to attempt it? He feared to learn that the small place he had occupied in her thoughts was now filled by others. Still he could not believe she was so indifferent as to forget their many exchanges of confidence, or those hours at her tea-table—hours when she had seemed so content to shut out the rest of the world for him. True, their talk had only been of books, of art and the theatre, of poetry and even philosophy; that ground where one reveals the innermost convictions and ideals. How unrestrained she had been! How sure of his understanding! Surely no one else, in so short a time, could take his place.

Well, he would make his decision when he got home.

Morton was now giving them instructions as to how they were to make the journey. The ship was to sail in a few days from Havre.

Most of them had forgotten what that port was like and therefore would have to be transported by the instructors. This removal was to begin at once. Morton warned them that if any of them failed to co-operate and help, by obeying orders, they would be left behind and must remain at Headquarters until another batch of the disabled were sent home.

At the news of sailing many of the men acted like schoolboys, shouting, singing, milling around excitedly. They seemed intoxicated with the idea of once more getting back to their own land. Morton smiled and remarked to one of the instructors:

"They think they are going to pick up their old lives just as they dropped them."

The more intelligent men were not so carried away. They realized that a new way of life lay before them, one they were utterly ignorant of. These men gave full attention to all that was told them and even tried to calm down the spirits of the others. Cummings was one of this group. He tried to talk to Hanson, whose loud voice was the first raised in the hullabaloo. Hanson was at his best when there was rioting of any kind. He was taller than most of the others and so made a fine drum major, a role he had always aspired to. He was now imitating the boom of a bass drum.

Boom! Boom! Boom, boom, boom!

The men formed in line and marched behind him. After this had been going on for some time, making a pandemonium for those who took no part in such a childish exhibition, Cummings went up to Hanson, the noisiest of the lot.

"Hanson, why don't you stop this and settle down and see if you can't help yourself a little? You don't want to be left here."

"Me? I'd like to see them try it. I'm going to be the first man on that boat."

"Don't fool yourself, Hanson. How are you going to get to Havre?"

"Never you mind. I'll be there all right."

"Look here, old man, can't you get it into your mind that unless you can concentrate steadily and powerfully enough, you will have to be taken there just as you were brought here from the dugout?"

This seemed to sober Hanson somewhat.

"What the hell are these people for only to take care of us? I gave my life for my country, didn't I? Well, then!"

Cummings patiently went over the ground again, trying to make him understand that there were few instructors and each had only so much mental power; when that was exhausted the men who were left would have to either help themselves or stay on at Headquarters.

Hanson then began to badger the instructors. As it turned out, they were so keen to be rid of him that they promised he should be taken among the first.

Potter was still sleeping and was left with others who had been so troublesome that they had been put to sleep.

Cummings was concerned for Brainard. He asked his grandfather what had happened that he had not returned.

"He's happier where he can see Carol Carlisle even though he cannot speak to her. He is going to wait here until she goes home."

"Tell him I shall hope to meet him somehow when he does come back."

At Havre, a few days later, the ship was loaded with wounded men and men who were shell-shocked—a polite way of speaking of those who had been driven insane by all they had gone through. Among the latter was Rosenberg. It was a very quiet little Rosenberg now; not the good-natured chatterbox that had bored the wounded at the base hospital, but a still, pale little man with wide, terrified eyes and a way of moving his lips in silent conversation with himself. He would smile in a vacant way when he was spoken to, but he seemed quite unconscious of what went on around him.

Flanagan, now able to go on one crutch, was among the wounded in another part of the ship. He did not even know that Rosenberg was aboard; not that he cared particularly, though he was sorry when he saw that the poor fellow's mind had broken.

On the voyage most of the men were very quiet, each simply waiting for the landing and mentally picturing the meeting with those who awaited them. Unseen by them were hundreds of the spirits of the slain who moved among them looking for old comrades.

Hanson was in his element when he got a few like-minded souls together on board, who then proceeded to make the voyage a continuous nightmare to the others.

Flanagan spent a good deal of the time lying down on the deck and thinking of Molly Burke. He had cabled her that he was coming and when he would arrive. She would be there on the dock, he knew. He could see her keen little face before him and her trig figure, so smart in her simple costume. Also he saw, as in a haze, the spirits in khaki all over the ship. What a lot of them! He never spoke to one of them and wished he could forget that they were there. He was glad to be away from Brainard and his constant begging him to make Miss Carlisle believe he was alive and still loving her. He was tired with the strain of Brainard's agonized pleadings day and night. He'd done all he could, and tried again, two or three times, to convince the girl that Brainard was really there. He had even delivered all the messages, but she had only smiled, in her kindly nurse-like way, and he knew she thought him slightly "shocked."

Well, thank God, he was out of all that now! He must concentrate on his own affairs. He must face the situation squarely now and he wondered how he was to make a living. Of course he was still a hospital case, but the wound was beginning to heal. Still he knew that he would be permanently lame. He would not be able to stand for long at a time, and the old job of clerking was out of the question. He wondered what he could turn to that would make a living. He only had his pharmacist's degree from the college, and that was no good unless he could keep on his feet. He worried a great deal over this. He wrote a regular and fairly legible hand and he was accurate. Perhaps the leader of his district would help him get some sort of small clerical job in the city government.

With this hope he quieted his nerves and centred his thoughts on the meeting with Molly. How sweet she was! He wished he had the money to marry her outright, but he must have a job first.

He hated the idea of having to go to a hospital again. Still, Molly would be coming to see him.

"Hello, Flanagan!"

Good God! Here was Cummings.

CHAPTER XXVI

❖

By this time Flanagan was practised in getting his thoughts enunciated. He replied to the greeting:

"Hello, Cummings!"

"We are both going home, but not to the same sort of world."

"No, I guess not."

"Aren't you surprised to be talking this way?"

"Oh, I'm getting used to it. I had Brainard after me every night at the hospital."

"Poor chap, he's still there, then?"

"Oh, yes. He's stuck on a nurse there and won't leave; but she's too hard-boiled. She won't believe it when I tell her he's there. He ought to get wise and come home and forget her."

Cummings was not very fond of Flanagan, but he recognized that here was a channel for communicating with the world.

"Flanagan," he said, "do you realize that you have a great gift? Something that could be used to help the world?"

Flanagan was not impressed.

"Oh, it's a damned nuisance. I've never told anybody but Brainard's girl, and she doesn't believe I can see and hear spirits. She thinks I'm off my base."

"But a great many people understand it and believe in communication after death."

"Well, I don't want to mess up in it. I don't see that it gets me anywhere."

"But can't you see, if everyone knew that we are all still living, we who've been killed in this rotten thing, they'd think twice before declaring another war because they'd know they'd have to meet their slaughtered soldiers when they die themselves."

"I don't believe it would make a damn bit of difference. They're out for profits and they'll take a chance on everything else."

"Listen, Flanagan! The world can't go on like this. We in the A.E.F. are only a few compared to the men who've been killed on both sides since the war began. A whole generation nearly. It's got to be stopped or there'll be nothing left."

"Well, you don't suppose I can stop it!"

"I don't know; but if you would write down the things I could dictate, perhaps we could make the world realize what it's headed for unless it puts an end to war."

"Say, what paper do you think would print that stuff?"

"I don't know, but we could try. Flanagan, it's a crime not to do what we can."

"Ah, forget it! I didn't make this war; neither did you."

"Flanagan, for God's sake don't take what I say like this. There are so many things I've learned since I came over here. I want to tell you about them."

"Say, listen! Cummings, I'm coming home to forget the war. You may be right, but what I want is to get this leg well and find some kind of a job. That's all I can bite off."

There it was, Cummings thought, every man for himself and the world headed for annihilation. Unless peace came soon, the best of American youth would fall, as had that of the enemy and the Allies.

The day the troop ship docked in New York the spirits of the doughboys were not so high as they had been on the way over. They knew the shock their crippled or disfigured bodies would be to their families. Flanagan felt relieved that he had no one but Molly to greet him.

A host of relatives and friends of Rosenberg were there, all waving to him and shouting their greetings. He came down the gangway, with the other shell-shocked men, in charge of Red Cross nurses. Many of these men could not even recognize their own, but stared with a sad, vacant gaze as though they were lost. Rosenberg recognized his sisters and their families when they got to him, but he was unable to make his mind adhere to any thought for long and, after the first greetings, he lapsed into that self-communion that shut out the rest of the world. He was fortunately unaware of their lamentations when his people saw the wreck that had been returned to them.

The nurses were familiar to him and he turned instinctively to them and was led away from his heart-broken sisters to be taken to a hospital for cases like his. He was one of the shock patients that the nurses found it easy to cope with. He was always obedient and never had the impulse to harm himself or another, but passed the days in the quiet peace that is almost idiocy.

Flanagan scanned the crowd of tense and longing faces each seeking out one of the khaki-clad figures moving so slowly off the ship. He had been right. There was Molly, looking thinner and somewhat older than he had pictured her. She had suffered in his absence and her face bore the marks of it. Still, she was as sweet and as dear to look upon as ever; more so, for he knew that it was because of him that she had lost some of her bloom. Her voice rang out in a shrill cry when she saw him, and like a mad thing she fought her way to him through the crowd, though the ones she pushed and shoved with such violence seemed unconscious of it, or of anything but that sad procession on the gangway. In the moment that he heard that cry, Flanagan lost all his manly shyness. He raised his cap with his free hand and sobbed out her name.

The little time her arms were about his shoulders was spent in silence. She clasped him as if to hold him for ever against the powers that had separated them. He could not speak and she had told him all he needed to know in their wordless meeting.

Cummings was one of the first souls off the ship. He wandered along the docks watching the pathetic reunions and the many small dramas that revealed a story of loyalty, faith, love, and the wreckage of hope. He saw Flanagan's meeting with his girl—a girl the little chap had never spoken of, in all the time of their association. What iron self-control Flanagan had! How beautiful the girl had been as she looked up at Flanagan, her eyes pouring into his the message from her soul.

Well, he had missed all that. What would he find now that would take its place? He was free now. Home and free!

Free for what?

He could visualize his old haunts, move along the familiar streets, and observe people. He could even go to Martin Fuller's office, his own business headquarters. He could even go to Martin's home and see Doris there.

No! That would be an intrusion. He must never yield to *that* temptation.

While he was moving along the street, he saw the spirits of those who had just landed. The men, most of them, had formed into line four abreast and, with Hanson at their head, they were singing as they came. They sang their marching songs and seemed to move in some sort of rhythm as they flowed through the traffic.

Cummings fell in. Why not?

They had marched down that same way to embark for France. The streets had been gay with flags then and the windows and pavements thronged with people cheering them on their way.

Now, with no banners flying, no bands blaring, no drums beating, and no crowds cheering, unseen and unheard the Dead marched back.

CHAPTER XXVII

❖

MANY of the spirits of those who had crossed on the ship with the disabled soldiers lived in localities at a distance. They had no way of reaching their old homes except by clinging to the trains that passed through their communities. They did not wish to remain in New York because they did not know the city and had no connections or associations there. They were strangers to the few spirits who had been with troops from New York, and they longed to be again with their own people and where they could roam about amid familiar scenes.

Most of the men had not been obedient to their instructors and learned to control their thoughts. They still lived, but that was all. They were automatically functioning in a body that seemed to be immortal. They were not even subject to hunger, thirst, or danger of illness, and they did not have to think of physical labour or making money. Those with the lower grade of mentality delighted in the idea of a life of continuous indolence. They seemed to think the sum of human happiness was reached when a career of complete idleness and irresponsibility lay before them.

The one who was most joyous over this prospect was Hanson. This was a real Paradise; he would never have to work again. True, he wished he could eat and drink and smoke, and have the pleasures of women and the excitements of gambling. Still, it was a joy to be alive and with no effort find oneself comfortable and free. He could roam where he liked and no police would interfere.

Some of the souls who had worked well under the instructors' guidance at Headquarters were now able to flash out—that is, to *think* themselves in their homes. Others, less able to control their minds, went through the streets until they found the places where their families lived.

Hanson had no family that he cared to see or whose whereabouts he knew. Soon he was alone. When he found himself deserted he felt somewhat dashed. To be alone was the last thing he had contemplated. He saw now that every man but himself had earthly ties. He began to realize that all his jokes and stories were already forgotten, and so was he.

What should he do now?

It looked as if there was no one to look after souls here as there had been in France. No one to take the responsibility for them. A wave of indignation swept over Hanson as he stood amid the traffic and hurrying crowds. This, then, was the reward for all he had suffered. He had given his life to his country and by every right should be treated as a martyr. Instead of that, here he was left to shift for himself. This was simply not to be borne. He pondered on what move he should make to get justice, but he came to no very definite conclusion. He wandered through the streets aimlessly as he let his wrath have full sway. He stood on corners and in doorways and watched the mortal men and women as they hurried along, most of them with driven, harassed expressions. In spite of his anger he smiled as he thought of their worries and problems, from which he was now completely freed.

When night came on, he decided to go down to the part of the city that was familiar to him. He had never been attracted to the beautiful streets and avenues; rather he liked to be where men of his own kind consorted. He moved on down near the waterside. There he found one of his old haunts and to his surprise many spirits were there also. They were the souls of men and women who were drawn back to the places where they could see life as they had lived it; souls unable to rise to any higher level because their sensual appetites still held them in thrall.

Hanson was delighted and in his element. He soon made friends with this group of Earthbound spirits.

These people could only mill around in the neighbourhoods they had known, as they had made no effort to improve their mentalities when, after death, they were given the teaching that would help them to rise above their old conceptions. They had no desire for any pleasures other than those they had known in their mortal bodies. Deprived of the joys of the senses, they still longed for them. They were able to gratify these longings, in some small measure, by clinging to the Earthly men and women who indulged in the same habits.

A small but rather attractive-looking spirit, the most manly specimen of the group, was trying to persuade the others to come to a meeting at a near-by square and listen to a teacher who would give them a lesson in mental control. The crowd jeered and laughed. They had been bored too often by that sort of thing. The speaker was trying to explain how foolish they were to keep themselves Earthbound when all the wonders of Etheric life could be theirs if they would learn how to control their minds.

He was apparently a man who had been one of them in his mortal life. He told them how he had been as great a drunkard and sexualist as any of them and that only his *will* had saved him, as their wills could do for them. He pointed out that they were wasting time and making their lives a danger to the mortals they clung to. Crimes were committed, he said, by spirits who clung to weak-minded mortals. He asked them if they meant to spend eternity in such company.

Hanson, keen to show off, took up the cudgels for the crowd and replied to the exhorter. He wanted to shine before this company of spiritual derelicts.

"Say, mister, what's the idea of making us all go to school? We want to live like we're grown up. I'm just off the battlefield over in France, where I was killed fighting for the Allies. Don't you suppose I want a little amusement after that? We're a nice jolly crowd here and we don't want to spend the time listening to all that stuff the teachers pull. Get a move on and let us alone. We can get some fun out of these live folks that are doing what we used to like to do. This is a free country. We're just having a little amusement and you come along and put a crimp in it."

The crowd shouted their approval and hailed Hanson as a man after their own hearts.

The soul who was trying to help them seemed to feel the hopelessness of his effort.

"You and the millions just like you are making the Earth life a terrible thing. When you crave drink you fasten your thought on a poor devil who has a weak will. He gets your thought and does your bidding. The same thing with those of you who took drugs, and you're not helping yourselves; you're only helping to ruin people who haven't the strength to resist you. Can't you realize the harm you are doing?"

Hanson shouted: "What difference does it make to you? You don't have to be responsible for us."

There was a roar from the spirits in the dive that expressed their entire agreement with Hanson's remarks. The little man disappeared. Hanson shouted to the crowd of souls:

"Now let's see what kind of hell-raising there is to be had down here when we don't have a regular body."

CHAPTER XXVIII

THERE was quite a ripple of excitement among the crowd of spirits when Hanson told them of his experiences in the army. He made a very fine record of his part in the fighting. Also he gave them a heroic picture of the way in which he lost his body. He was the bravest man in his company, if he did say it himself. He was not a particularly enthusiastic American, but he really felt so patriotic that he said:

"This is God's own country, the only country that's fit for a white man to live in; and when we get the Heinies licked I'm going to go back into a body and live in it again. This is no fun when you can't feel or taste or smell. What's the good of it? I'd rather be dead."

There was general assent to this. Only one man failed to cheer. He was a tough-looking customer and had been making signs to one of the lot to come along with him.

They drifted away, and when they were beyond earshot of the others, the larger man said:

"I'm going to get square with an old enemy of mine. He used to work alongside of me when I was alive, and he had a mean, underhanded way of making the boss think I loafed on the job. I swore I'd get even some day. Well, I never got the chance to get square. I've waited here, near the wharves, to find him ever since I croaked ten years ago. Now he's showed up at last."

"How can you get even?" his vicious-looking companion asked.

"You wait and see. I need some help, though. You like to show your power over the folks that can't think very strong, so I know you'll be a pal."

"What's the game?"

"It's just to make somebody bump that fellow off."

"I like your nerve. Why should I bump off anybody that I don't give a damn about?"

"I'd do it myself only I can't fix my mind so strong as you can yours. Come on, be a pal!"

After a few more arguments he went along and the two came upon a man standing in the doorway of a mean tenement.

"There he is. That's the guy."

"Well, I can't do him any harm. I can only make someone else, someone that's got a body, do the trick."

"All right, we'll wait around until he goes to work. There's plenty of dumb ones down at the docks."

The two waited and then trailed after their man, who went to take his place in the shift that was loading a giant steamship.

When they came to the gateway of the docks they stopped, but the man they had followed went through to his work.

"Wait here. I'll soon pick out a guy that will do as I make him."

They waited for a few moments watching for the perfect mind to do as he was bid. Not many had filed by before the choice was made. They followed the labourer who was marked as just right for the work.

The man who was to be "paid off" set to work with the others loading the cargo with a truck. Back and forth he went, in the line of men with the freight. Among them was the chosen avenger.

The first time that he paused in his labour, the soul who was to make the errand a success went close to him and said with determination:

"See that fellow coming toward you? He says he's going to *get* you."

He repeated this until the labourer's vacant expression turned to a look of suspicion and his eyes followed the man he thought was his enemy. Over and over again the spirit voice kept saying:

"If you don't get him first, he'll kill you."

The labourer put down his truck and stood waiting for the other to come along with his load again. The strong-willed soul turned to the other:

"You see? He'll do whatever I say. He's what they call a moron, a fellow that's weak in his head."

"Great! I wish I had your power!"

"We strong-minded spirits have more to do with things on Earth than they think."

"Here comes the ——" He indicated his old enemy.

There was presently the sound of a yell, a volley of curses, and the work was done. The weak-minded labourer was on top of the other, beating him. Immediately a crowd formed around them, and when the victim was rescued he was unconscious. Soon he was out of his body and stood looking down at it in amazement.

"What did he do that to me for? I don't even know that guy."

"That's what you got for doing me out of my job, Andy."

Andy turned and saw his old fellow worker.

"Hello, Frank! What's happening here?"

"Just evening things up, that's all."

"Say, you died a long time ago. I guess I must be going crazy."

"Sure, I'm dead and so are you now. So we're quits at last."

And Frank walked away with his friend who had accommodated him so neatly.

"Now I can see you're a master mind, all right. You certainly put it over with that other one."

"Yes, he'll probably get the chair for it, unless they call him insane when he tells them he doesn't know why he did it."

"But he's innocent."

"What do you care? You got what you wanted."

The murderer was in a daze. He had been sure he ought to kill that stranger and now he wondered what had made him do it. His weak mind was confused.

The day he was executed he went to the chair still wondering about the voice he had heard so plainly.

All this time Hanson stayed with his new friends, spiritual derelicts, souls who preyed upon the weak-willed. All forms of vice were their delight and they made up their life by suggesting to moronic mortals, drug addicts, sexualists, and drunkards all sorts of depraved acts. This could only be done by those with enough thought-power to dominate them. Others, as mentally weak, revelled in reliving the vices they could not forget.

This was the Hell of the Etheric plane, where degraded souls preyed upon the living. Most of these were women who were a prey to their lusts. They were of every grade of life, creatures who could not force their minds away from the past.

Hanson found them quite congenial.

CHAPTER XXIX

❖

WHEN Cummings left the parade he moved down the side street to the hotel where he had lived for several years before he had gone to France with the troops. He had left his books, his pictures and little art objects in his suite and locked the door. This had been his personal home; now it was a no man's land. Word of his death had been published and his next of kin, a cousin whom he scarcely knew, would soon be claiming his belongings along with what other estate he had left.

He was able, very easily, to make his way to his old quarters, though he did not use his thought-force, but moved through the hotel corridors and up the stairways to his rooms. The door was no obstacle, and as he passed into his sitting-room he marked the unoccupied look of the place. The shades were drawn and in the dimness he saw another form, that of a woman. She was standing by a little table where, among other things, he had kept a small framed photograph of himself.

He was startled, and before he could decide what the trespasser was doing there, the figure turned and faced him. It was Doris; she was weeping.

What was she here for? Could she be weeping for him?

The thought was almost shattering. He had never dared believe she was in love with him, she who was so self-possessed, so perfectly in command of her emotions. Could she care like this?

He went up to her and put his arms about her. He spoke her name and all the endearing names he had treasured for her in his thoughts.

What a perfect home-coming!

Here was the woman of his heart in his home, waiting for him; and her tears revealing the love he had wished for through the years. It was worth dying for. This was what he had dreamed of in France. In moments when he tried to forget the horrors around him, he had many times sought escape in the thought of his love for Doris and in fancy held her close and claimed her.

But he was forgetting now that she could not know how near he was, or that he knew now of her love for him. He could hear her repeating his name over and over again and holding his framed face to her lips.

He was so exalted by the revelation of her love for him that for the moment he forgot that death separated them and he poured out to her all that he had kept locked within himself through the years. She was the prize he had wanted, the supreme gift of life that he desired beyond all else. He was too much of a poet at heart not to clothe his love in beauty, so that all he was now saying was like a hymn to love and to her.

Never had he realized how dear her tears could be. She had seemed quite apart from those women who found relief in tears. Her splendid mental balance had always been her great charm, and he saw now that it had only been a glorious defence.

This surging joy that he felt made up to him for the lonely and barren hours he had spent in this room where they were now united. He could never doubt life again, for he had come to know the fulfilment of his deepest need.

These moments came to an end when he realized that she could not know his feelings or even sense his presence. She had been in his embrace and he had poured out his heart to her, yet she was unconscious of him.

Finally, when he became calm enough to reason, he made an effort to impress his mind on hers. The first thought that came to him was: "She must know that I am here." He fixed his mind on that.

There was no sign, at first, that his thought had reached her or that she was conscious of him. Then, suddenly, she raised her head and looked up at him. He almost thought she saw him, for she seemed to be looking into his eyes. He concentrated then on the words:

"Doris, you know that I love you."

He kept repeating this thought with the full force of his mind. Then, as if unconscious that she had done so, Doris spoke his name. Her voice had a thrilling note that he had never heard before and the words came:

"Where are you, Dent? Somehow, somewhere, I must meet you again."

He knew now that her soul had got his message and that she would never again suffer that sense of despair and loss.

When they had made their love known to each other, in this mystical way, a calm seemed to descend on both of them. He was certain now that in this meeting she had been made his, and his course in the future was clear—to wait for her coming and to make the best of life.

The time for parting had come. He was sure she would never visit this room again. As it had been the first lovers' meeting, so it would be the last, and he wanted to speak the farewell that was in his heart. He bent his mind to the words:

"Be still, Doris, and let us say good-bye."

She had opened the door, but suddenly pressed it shut, standing against it with her head thrown back and her eyes closed as if in silent farewell.

The words came slowly and clearly from him:

"My beloved, all that I am and ever shall be is yours. I now pledge my life to you and I take your love, to have and to hold eternally. My love will be with you always; and may you know the same sweet peace that you have brought to me. Good-bye, my own!"

A moment of silence; the door opened again and she was gone.

He did not try to follow her, but stood as she had left him.

The light that shone from him irradiated the room.

CHAPTER XXX

❖

THE street seemed strange and unfamiliar to Doris Fuller when she went from the hotel. She had asked to be permitted to visit Mr. Dent Cummings's rooms and, after considerable argument and the presentation of credentials, she had been allowed to spend half an hour there. As she stood in the street she was conscious of returning as from a long journey. The idea of time was like a shock, for she felt as though she had been where time had ceased. Now she must put herself into the mood in which she could competently make the various moves and meet the many conditions that constituted the days of her life.

Her love for Dent Cummings was now for ever entombed. She had never dared own it, even to herself, she was so sure that she was above such weakness. She had been content in her marriage with Martin and felt secure in the thought that the life she had with him was as happy as any woman could expect. Martin was kind and devoted and she had been able to find amusement in the task of helping him discover talented writers.

When she met Dent Cummings she was positive that he was simply a fascinating drifter. Still, he had stirred something within her and made her aware that she was not quite so safe as she had supposed. He was disarming and she came to feel that they could continue in the delightful friendship that had become a precious thing in her life. She bore his conscription with fortitude. He seemed, in their few meetings before he went to France, to have but one idea—to be humorous and light-hearted about it. There were terrible moments when she knew that life without him would be a waste of dullness.

Martin, like most American husbands, had been good-natured and tolerant about his wife's friends. Dent Cummings was his friend as well and had been, even in college. Besides, Cummings was a valuable man in his business. So Martin saw no harm in Doris's seeing Dent whenever she chose. Anyway, he could be sure of Doris; she was too cold, too poised, to be susceptible.

There had been flashing seconds when Doris had to call up all her arts of self-command when she and Dent were together, and when it came to the good-bye she had wanted to say: "I shall not live until you are back again. You are taking something of me with you."

But she had been the good friend only, who bade him "good luck and safe return." Martin had showed more feeling than she in their farewell.

From then on, Doris threw herself into the work of helping in the various organizations that supported the war. She gave herself no time to think. Her letters to Dent were guarded and a complete mask for her real feelings. His letters were charming and the many little sketches of the lighter side of the life he was now living were so impersonal that they gave her confidence that her own feelings were wholly unknown to him, much less returned.

Then came the news of his death. She was like a woman of stone for days after that. Life seemed unreal, remote, with little relation to herself. Martin would talk about it; that was the hardest thing to bear, to hear *his* name and the details of his regiment's part in the action. He was among the missing, but the *way* of his death had been reported by his officers.

When her nerves could bear it no longer, she had gone to the place that he had lived in, where she could perhaps get some chance to face it all with herself. When she arrived there and had to argue, produce credentials, give her name and her husband's, she was not concerned with what the hotel people might think of her visit, but only to be alone where Dent had been and, in her imagination, picture him as he had once been—the soul of those rooms.

When she had dismissed the servant who unlocked the door, she went about, taking into account the titles of his books, the pictures on the walls, the small works of art that stood on his tables, and the lovely pieces of pottery that gave so much colour and character to the sitting-room.

When, at last, she had made a survey of all the things that could speak to her of him, she took his pictured face in her hands and the tide, so long held in check, swept the last of her defences away.

Now it was all over! Her task would be to forget him.

Forget! No. She would not even try to forget.

She would *remember*.

This love should make its home within her consciousness and there she would retreat in the moments when her life became too difficult. This love should be her secret spring, the fountain from which she would draw the strength to meet the years.

CHAPTER XXXI

❖

OF all the wounded that had been returned from France, the first
to leave the hospital was Flanagan. He had made the most of the
enforced idleness to write letters to those he thought might help him
to secure a clerical position in one of the city departments. He was
not very fortunate, though the replies he received in some instances
were most polite. In answer to his other letters there was only
silence. He made a mental note of the latter. No man should snub
him like that and get away with it. He would make it his business to
investigate the gentleman and see why he, a voter, a good district
worker, was ignored. He made no effort to use his war record or
his wound as a lever to get political help, though he did feel that
they should entitle him to some consideration.

He was now getting a full and clear perspective of just how little
he could expect from the political patriots who had been so vocal
in their enthusiasm over the A.E.F. The bitter realization that the
returned soldiers were now not wanted in civil life had been growing, and now he knew that, handicapped as he was, he was absolutely on his own.

Only one human being could be counted on—Molly. Well, he
must break into something and marry her. She would keep her
job, but he must be able to shoulder the major part of their ex-
penses.

He called upon his old employer, Mr. Green, manager of the chain drug stores. Mr. Green was very busy but condescendingly gave him ten minutes. His manner indicated that he considered Flanagan's call a social one.

"Well, I see you've had a bad mix-up with the Boches." This with a look at Flanagan's crutch.

"Yes. I guess you know what we had over there."

"Pretty tough, I suppose. I don't get time to follow it all up in the newspapers. You know we have to keep things moving here. Well, I'm glad to see you, Flanagan, it was nice of you to drop in."

"Mr. Green, I know I can't do my old work, with this game leg, but the prescription department—well, I hoped you'd let me take that work. I can move around out of sight of the customers and I guess you know my record for accuracy."

Mr. Green looked down at his desk and was silent for a moment; then without raising his eyes:

"You'll have to realize, Flanagan, that we've built up our organization since you left, and it isn't easy to make changes now. The men we've got are all satisfactory. I can't let a man out just to make a place for you. You can understand that."

"I see."

Flanagan struggled up from the chair and put his crutch under his arm.

"Drop in again and tell me all about it."

Flanagan did not answer, but nodded a good-bye and hobbled out and down to the street.

"And he'd like to hear all about it!"

He went back to his little room and lay on his bed.

"So they're all organized now and I'm out of it!"

He saw that all the *glory* was out of it too. The returned soldier was not wanted. He was a misfit. His place in the world was filled by a man who'd somehow missed the draft.

Where were all those solid citizens who not so long ago had made them feel that when they came back from fighting *the town would be theirs*?

He began to search the newspaper advertisements. He stumped along the streets looking for any job he could fill. The answer was always the same. He went to his district leader, who seemed to find it not easy to remember him. Flanagan found it difficult to ask for assistance from this hard-eyed citizen, but he managed to stammer out his request for help to get into a desk job, where he could earn a salary in some sort of public service.

"Oh? . . . Well! . . . You don't look exactly up to a job yet. Better take it easy. That leg of yours ought to get you a pension; then you won't need a job."

"But I want to get married. I want to make my living. I'm only twenty-six. I don't want to loaf for the rest of my life."

"I'm sorry, my lad, but I haven't any pull. The crowd that's in now won't do anything for me."

That was a lie. He had the power and Flanagan knew it.

So this was the man for whom he had worked, passing out hand-bills, doing clerical work nights at headquarters, the man whose speeches he had cheered!

All he could think of now was how to take his revenge. It wasn't a thing he could accomplish now, but one day he would make things even between them. His rage gave him a sort of comfort.

The next few weeks were spent in the same fruitless search. He was not beaten, but he was low in funds and began to wonder where he could turn for help. He had spent his little store lavishly, at first for presents and treats for Molly. She saw how weary he looked in the evening when they would be together in a restaurant or watching a motion picture.

What he loved best were the times when they sat in the parks and in the shadows he could have her close to him. Her endearments and her shining eyes, so filled with love—these gave him courage for the next day's search.

At last he was forced to admit that he was beaten. There was no place for him and he might as well face it.

Hanson! Brainard! Cummings! Potter! They were the lucky ones. The men who go to war and come back maimed are worse than dead!

CHAPTER XXXII

❖

HANSON was not satisfied for very long simply to be a spectator and watch mortals enjoy the dissipations he had formerly indulged in. He also wore out his welcome among the spirits of his own kind. After his stories had been repeated and his jokes laughed at once, they lost interest in him.

Their lives were spent in telling of their *own* experiences as well as in giving attention to new arrivals who might thrill them with fresh anecdotes. Unable to rise above the memory of their past degraded lives, they were not capable of concentrating on anything higher. They existed and that was all. Now and then there would be an instance of one who might be reclaimed, but these were rare exceptions. The teachers and Masters gave them every chance and explained the way of progress to them, but this called for an effort of the mind which was beyond them.

One day Hanson decided to try to locate the hospital where Rosenberg must be now. He was in doubt about finding it, but he made inquiries of the spirits who seemed to be of a better class than the ones who had lately been his companions. They told him the injured soldiers had been taken to a hospital on the East Side. So Hanson, who was familiar with the locality, managed to find it.

He was curious to see what had happened to Rosenberg. He had recognized the little chap on the boat, but did not know what had been wrong with him. Rosenberg was so quiet on the voyage over that Hanson concluded he must have been badly wounded though he saw no bandages on him.

Hanson was getting bored with spirit life and wondered how he could find a more lively existence. What he most longed for was *food;* that had been his principal passion and objective in life. The rations of a soldier had been far from his standard, but now he was deprived of the enjoyment of the pleasures of the palate altogether. He felt that he must find a way of getting around that. Life without eating was not to be borne.

These were his thoughts as he reached the particular hospital he was looking for. When he passed through its corridors and wards he saw many ruins of what had once been fine specimens of physical manhood, the best their country had produced. The sight did not in the least affect him. He had seen far worse on the field and he was not one to lament over the misfortunes of others.

He found no one that he recognized and was about to leave when he sighted Rosenberg sitting beside a window in one of the wards.

As he went to him, Hanson noted that he seemed to be talking to himself. So *that* was what ailed him! *Shock.* What a mess it had been! Here was his buddy making conversation with himself and clean out of the game. Well, he would see if he could talk to him anyway. So far he hadn't been able to make anybody with an Earthly body hear him, but he'd try again.

When he came near and began to speak, he could see that Rosenberg seemed to be listening, for he had stopped his talk with himself and was quiet, with an expression as if he heard.

Hanson came close to him and spoke his name. The poor vacant face lit up. Hanson repeated it. Rosenberg stood up and looked around as though he expected to see the one who was calling him.

"No, no, sit down. I'm here, right in front of you."

Rosenberg sat down again and seemed to be looking at Hanson; his lips moved, but no sound came.

"See here, Rosenberg, I'm Hanson, your old buddy. I got mine all right, but this here death don't seem to kill you. It jest makes a damn spirit out of you."

He was sure Rosenberg saw him; for a moment there was a look of intelligence as he muttered:

"Hanson, I heard you calling me."

"Sure I'm calling you. I've come to see you."

But the cloud had come over the mechanism of his brain and he was seemingly unaware of Hanson now.

There were plenty of cases of shock in this room and Hanson saw now that the place was an insane ward. Some of the men were like Rosenberg, sitting quietly off by themselves and giving no trouble. Some were murmuring childishly to themselves. Others were in a state of complete despair and wore an expression of horror. Memories of the things they had seen were so strongly impressed on their minds that they still saw the horrors of the battlefields.

When Hanson had made the rounds of this ward he returned to Rosenberg, who was again having a muted conversation with himself.

"Why do you make me go back to fight? I'm a Jew. I don't hate Germans, they never have done me any harm. My father was a German Jew. We came to America because all kinds of people live there. Don't send me back. I'm no good at killing. You can see I'm a Jew. We ain't soldiers. Please let me stay here. I'll be quiet. I won't make no trouble. . . . Doctor, you see how sick I am. I'm sick because you want to send me back to the front again. . . . I'm a Jew, doctor. That means I wasn't never trained to kill people. . . . Won't you *please* let me stay here? I'll lie down quiet so nobody will know I'm here. I won't talk to nobody. I'll just lie still and be safe here. Please! I ask you! Please to let me stay— please!"

And so on over and over again he relived those hours when he was begging to be allowed to stay behind the lines. Hanson listened to the continuous murmuring and whispering, and in the pauses he would speak to him.

"Rosenberg! It's me. It's Hanson. Shut up and listen. Shut up, I tell you."

The whispering died away and the black eyes were filled with tears.

"My old buddy, Hanson. He's gone. He won't help me no more. He's gone west. I'll never see him again. . . . Doctor, can't you let me stay?"

And it was beginning all over again. Hanson was losing patience.

This was about the middle of the day and the men were taken to dinner in a room off their ward. The sight of the food on the table gave Hanson a thrill of joy.

The men, ranged on either side of it on benches, mechanically began to eat. Rosenberg sat near the end of the long board.

Then there came into Hanson's mind the idea of trying to get inside the body of Rosenberg. He had seen such things done down on the waterfront. Spirits that craved drink had simply gone right into the body of the mortal who was about to drink a glass of liquor, and after a time they would appear again and say they had enjoyed it. Now if *he* could only do that, he might enjoy the plateful of good food that Rosenberg was scarcely touching.

He began to think of himself as Rosenberg, to get the image of him in his mind and to imagine himself as the same size as the little chap. When he had practised this a few times he seemed to be able to contract himself, and also he felt that he *was* Rosenberg. Suddenly he found himself *in the body of Rosenberg*, and with the power to move, to speak, to *eat*.

When the first excitement of this experience had passed he began to shovel in the food. What a treat! He was not critical of the menu now, but made contented little noises and licked his lips with appreciation.

The men near him paid no attention. The waiters, though, watched him with amazement. This was a sudden change in the little fellow who usually ate barely enough to keep himself alive. The few men at the table who were not so far gone as not to observe the change in him finally commented on it and watched him as he greedily wolfed his food.

The waiters reported this astonishing change to the nurses, who in turn reported it to the doctors. The doctors took it as a good sign. There were features of Rosenberg's improvement, however, that puzzled them. He no longer sat continually, quietly whispering to himself. He was now noisy and profane and at times went among the other men telling them obscene jokes.

Rosenberg was never the same again, and from a mild case of "shock" he became one of the mysterious cases that baffled the doctors and nurses. He seemed to be the opposite of everything he had been before. Whenever his sisters and friends came to see him he was often so coarse and made such indecent personal remarks that they were horrified and cut their visits short.

Hanson enjoyed all this. He had the body of his buddy now to use as he pleased and whenever he pleased. If only he could get out of the hospital with it he might enjoy himself still further. Still, he missed the sense of his bigness, his tall figure, his giant strength.

This little body seemed a poor one for him to have to wear. All the same it was flesh and blood and he would make the best of it.

Rosenberg was no longer the pale wraith he had been. Since he had taken to eating so gluttonously he had become a little fat man. Hanson, when he was *out* of the body of his old buddy, was amused to see this change. He frequently left him at night and went down among his old acquaintances, where he liked to tell them about it. They were old hands at obsessing and were not particularly impressed.

The doctors found Morris a very "interesting" patient and made lengthy reports on the strange case of Private Morris Rosenberg.

CHAPTER XXXIII

❖

THE war was over. All the spirits of the dead in the A.E.F., as well as those souls who had received them, had now returned, and the broken men also.

The able-bodied soldiers were coming back as fast as the ships could bring them. Chris Goertsch was among these. He had come through in perfect wholeness, as he was sure he would. That is, he was physically whole. He had not had a wound or been shocked and he had made a fine record. His superiors noted that he had carried his wounded comrade Flanagan off the field under fire, his record for taking prisoners was high, and he had made his mark in hand-to-hand fighting.

On his return Goertsch found himself a real victor. Photographs of him were taken, reporters interviewed him, and later on he was given a medal. When he had been glorified and made much of for a week, he sank out of sight. Then he had a good time, for a while, taking in the shows and the dance halls.

He was surprised to find that the girls were not so keen for the soldiers as they had been before he sailed away to the war. He was also surprised at the manner in which the men and women on the street viewed his uniform with calm indifference. What had changed everybody so? He was shocked and angry at this apparent betrayal.

After he had been home a month or so the war began to recede in his mind until it became a misty dream of a time when life was exciting and thrilling; when the sound of the scream and thunder of guns and an accompaniment of crashing noises had set his blood coursing at a faster pace and sharpened all his faculties. Now there was only the routine of fancy girls and the theatres; they seemed pretty tame after the big show he had taken part in. Not much of a life!

When he looked ahead he decided that he would never go on the milk route again. That was a job for a man who didn't know any better. He was now the idol of his father and mother and his younger brothers and sisters, so he didn't have to worry about the future; there was always his parents' flat where he could live; but he didn't want that. What he wanted was to get into something that would put a "kick" into life.

Goertsch saw his chance at last. He joined a group of men who were getting rich by bringing liquor into the country in violation of the laws against its importation. Chris was in his element. Here was excitement, danger; and with big money, too, compared to the pay of a doughboy or a milkman. The "rum-running," as they called it, gave him just the thrill he was after. His family, honest, hard-working folk, never knew just what his job was. He was absent a great deal of the time, and when he was home he discouraged any inquiries about his work. He was never ill-natured and he was generous with his money. Still, there was something mysterious about it.

After a time Goertsch grew weary even of this occupation. He told himself it was not a game that would make him rich. He was only an employee and his bosses got the big money. He was too much of a rounder now to have any illusions about honest poverty.

He wanted riches, money to squander on expensive women, on gambling. He wanted smart clothes and knew he could cut a striking figure in them. He longed for a fine motor car, to travel to the strange places he had seen in the picture theatres.

Later on, when he fell in with a gang of fellows who were out for the same things, he was easily persuaded to join them. He knew that he ran desperate risks of being caught and sent to prison, but he was sure they would never get him and that he bore a charmed life, just as he had in France.

These were the days after the war when some of the returned soldiers, hardened to the idea of living dangerously, of holding life cheap, were willing to take long chances.

Goertsch and his mates were successful in a number of robberies, and pay-roll thefts. They killed several people and maimed others in these operations. There were times when the officers of the law were very near to closing in on Chris, but somehow he always got away. This gave him a still firmer belief in his own immunity.

When he was safely through with several of his exploits, he found he was the owner of quite a small fortune in cash. He did not know how to dispose of it. To bank it was not feasible for a time and to spend too much would attract attention to himself.

Some time after these adventures he had a sudden impulse to look up the two survivors of his old unit. He seldom thought of them, but with no work and plenty of idle time he decided to see what had become of Rosenberg and Flanagan. When he tried to trace them he was surprised to learn that Rosenberg was a permanent shock case. Well, he wasn't interested in visiting a man who was off his head, though some time, perhaps, he would drop in and take a look at the poor devil.

One day as he came out on the street after a session of playing pool, he recognized Flanagan limping by on his crutch. He was out of uniform and his clothes looked shabby. Chris hailed him. Flanagan was dazzled at the resplendence of his late comrade and smiled his little wry, cryptic smile. They stood for a few moments and exchanged the usual greetings.

"What you doing now, Flanagan?"

"Looking for a job. Something I can do that will let me sit down."

"Any prospects?"

"Not yet."

"You sure have been out of luck."

"Looks that way."

"Can I do anything for you?"

"Not unless you can tip me off where I can get a job."

"I don't know of any, but I can let you have some coin."

Flanagan flushed. "I can't pay back a loan unless I can get work."

"Never mind. I'm not suffering for it. Here."

Goertsch pulled out a roll of bills and thrust several of them into Flanagan's hand. Then with a grin he touched his hat in the old salute and went on.

"So long! And just forget it!"

Tears were in Flanagan's eyes. Here was the last man he could have expected help from. He was filled with self-reproach for the many times he had cursed Goertsch for a big moron. It was Goertsch who had carried him off the field, and now he had rescued him a second time.

Molly was to meet him a little later when she left her work. Now he could give her a bit of good news at last. He was so far from his old self that even this money, which was pure charity, seemed like a direct act of Providence. He could treat Molly and himself to a really good dinner that evening.

Molly was very quiet that night. She knew now that his quest for employment was hopeless. There was only one way for them—to marry and have a room together, the burden to be hers. Would he ever consent to that?

If only he was not so proud! But he was so eager to play a man's part in everything; he had such a sense of decency, and his dignity was so fine. Molly was sure he was the only man who had these qualities in such full measure. She did not analyse and classify his virtues in this manner—that was beyond her—but she felt and knew these things of him. Her love had grown even stronger as the weeks and months revealed the gallantry of his losing fight.

Flanagan never complained; he would not whine, he would find a way yet. Molly was worth it all if in the end he could make their happiness.

When the time came to say good-night, Molly stood in her doorway and looked at his thin, drawn face, which bore the record of the weary months of frustration. She began to cry.

"Oh, let's not fight any longer! Let's be together. We can't go on like this. I can't bear it."

He was taken unawares and, for the moment, could only hold her close and reassure her with endearments. She went on:

"We'll both be old and tired and we won't care any more. We must have our life now, while we're young. Can't you see how we're wasting our lives? For what? Just because things aren't easy, and for pride."

He tried to steady his voice.

"Now, Molly, you can't call it pride because I won't tie you down until I can make a living. That's only decent."

"I don't care what you call it. I know we are fools to try to go on like this any longer."

The morning light was coming before he finally consented, with the thought that, at least, he had enough in his pocket now to pay the priest and a few weeks' room rent, thanks to Chris Goertsch. After that he would find *something*. He and Molly would belong to each other, and that would surely bring good luck.

So he tried to make peace with himself, but he was humiliated and ashamed. He knew he had betrayed his manhood.

Molly was too fond to care.

CHAPTER XXXIV

❖

THE war had been over some time before Carol Carlisle was free to return; now she was homeward bound. When at last the day came to be sent back with other nurses, she went on board the ship with a heavy heart. All her hopes lay buried in a field in France, a white cross marking the place.

Carol was not melancholy; rather she was merry, in spite of that steady pull at the centre of her being. It was home she was going to, where loving friends would greet her. People would offer sympathy over Gordon's death; they would even act as though she had been left a widow. Her work in France would be praised and she would have a place of honour in her little city.

All this she was grateful for. Still she knew she could not remain at home. A visit, a reunion, and she must be away. To be where Gordon's name was spoken would still hurt too much. To go back to New York and work in the veterans' hospital, that was her plan, and already she had applied for a position there.

When she walked the deck at night, under the stars, she felt less alone than when she was surrounded by others. It was then she could think of Gordon and fancy that he was beside her, they two making their love known to each other with only the night as a witness.

Often Carol had imagined Gordon speaking to her; she seemed

to feel, rather than hear, his voice. Then she knew her nerves were making her fanciful and she put the idea out of her mind. There was really no reason for these sudden impressions, she argued; yet there was all the time the most definite, though delicate, sense of a presence near whenever she was alone. This had been a frequent occurrence.

What a state she was in! She decided that she must take a good rest. She would sleep as much as possible and get back to her normal condition, which was that of perfect health.

Then the time would come when she was off guard and again she almost saw someone beside her. In these moments she would sometimes cry out: "Gordon!" That would bring her to herself and she would be horrified that she had been thrown off her centre.

The rest she craved was an absolute change: out of uniform, and completely immersed in the society of people who talked of the things she loved: books, music, art. The small chatter of social life she cared nothing for, but she had always been a lover of the beautiful. Perhaps if she could be bathed once more in the glories of the imagination of rare creative souls she could recover her mental poise and be free of these strange delusions.

While she was happy in those fleeting moments, she was terrified as she thought of them. She feared she was going the same road as that poor fellow Flanagan, who perhaps by now was in some hospital for the insane.

Then came the most trying experience of the voyage. Carol was sitting on deck beside another nurse; they were silent as they reclined in their chairs. Carol was not asleep, yet she seemed not fully awake. She had a clear vision of Gordon in his uniform standing in front of her and saying, with his old smile:

"We are going home at last."

She was so astonished she could not answer, and when she made an effort to do so, Gordon had gone.

What was it that she had seen?

Was she already so ill that she could fancy anything as real as this?

The nurse beside her was serenely looking over the very spot where Gordon had stood; apparently she had seen and heard nothing.

It was all over in an instant. The momentary impression was gone and Carol wondered if she really hadn't fallen asleep for a moment and dreamed this. When she finally decided that she *had* been asleep she was satisfied.

Carol was too much of a realist to make this a serious matter. She was sure of herself when she put such occurrences in a pigeon-hole and marked them *Delusions;* yet she was quite aware of the sudden joy she felt when she experienced them.

What a light they shed on the theory of wish-fulfilment, of repressions, and psychoanalysis! She could now testify to the soundness of this modern school of mental science.

This had been the way her thought ran and she comforted herself with these explanations.

Meantime she was all that an efficient war nurse should be. Most of the women who were on board were made of the stern stuff that had not weakened under the strain; she must be equally strong.

These were Carol's reflections as she turned to her homeland ready to make a new life for herself.

Many of the war nurses came home to return to their old ways of life. A few had been made conscious of the need of a great movement for peace and declared themselves ready to work for it. The scenes they had witnessed, the broken bodies they had nursed, had made them fully aware of the stupid cruelty of war and its senselessness as a means of demonstrating political theories.

Carol was in sympathy with the idea of a peace movement, but she was not convinced that it could be of any real use in abolishing war. Peace she knew had been preached for two thousand years, and the result was a war in which ten million men were killed and three times as many maimed. How many millions were brutalized, insensitized, and made unfit for civilization, would never be known. The ideal of force, of the rule of Might, had been taught to every soldier on every front. Carol was not caught by the word "peace." She knew there was no peace. Her mind was too clear to believe that the cry "Peace! Peace!" would make lambs of men who had been turned into wolves.

CHAPTER XXXV

❖

Most men in Brainard's place would have wearied of being alone, with no way of making themselves more than an occasional shadow on the consciousness of the one they were living near. Still, that is what he had made up his mind to do. He was sure that in time he could make himself visible to Carol. The long weeks and months in the places where she was on duty after the armistice had made no change in his determination to be near her; to wait until she returned home and go with her.

There was a time when his grandfather came frequently to see him, but he had now gone home and there was only silence. In those months when he was a lone soul drifting through the hospitals where Carol nursed, he began to think and to understand the things he had failed to heed when he had been at Headquarters. Also he pondered all that had been told him by his grandfather and realized how comparatively little power he had.

This was no life for anyone. He could not help Carol; he could not even make her believe that he was still a living being and still loving her. What good was such a life?

Suddenly he began to hear the doctors, the nurses, and the soldiers talk of going home.

What a relief it would be!

He was not the most ardent of patriots, but he was keen to have some companionship with his own kind once more. He wanted to be in the company of men, to see his mother and father again, though he knew his death would be a deep shadow on their lives. Still, he could have the happiness of seeing them, and perhaps there might be a chance to make his presence known to them.

When the time came to leave France he was nearer to a feeling of peace than he had known since he left the shores of the United States. Carol had much more leisure now and he could be close to her in their walks on deck even though she did not know it. He got her thoughts of him and he tried to impress his own on her mind. When he finally made an effort so powerful that Carol saw him, he smiled and said:

"We are going home at last."

Instead of the joy he expected, she seemed terrified and almost immediately went below. So even the sight of him was useless! What good had his momentary revelation been when she was not even willing to accept his presence as real?

Had it all been a waste of time to stay close to her? How could love be so blind? What happiness was there ahead for them if she believed him to be out of existence?

He was not bitter, but he felt let down.

Why was she so keen to deny anything that could not be accounted for on the plane of psychoanalysis? What joy was there in life on the basis of such a theory?

Of course he had to acknowledge that up to the time of his own death he himself had held the same opinions.

There were several people on board who, like himself, were in their Etheric bodies, men killed in France. There was also a man in charge of them, an instructor, whose work was to care for the soldier spirits. Brainard made it a point to be with him most of the time after Carol refused to admit his presence. He determined to make up for some of the time he had wasted. This teacher, a man evidently of long experience in helping those fresh from Earth life, gave Brainard rather special attention and even said he thought him ready to become a promising student.

When Brainard explained that he hoped to make a contact somehow with one he loved and perhaps convince his parents that he still lived, the instructor was not too encouraging.

"When you have no training in conserving and using your mental force, which is the only power we have here, it is doubtful if you can accomplish much. However, if you decide to return to New York we have a post there where our members are easily reached by Earthbound souls, which of course you are now, and you can let us know when you are ready to enter a class for study. We are known as the White Brotherhood. This is a secular order, and our aim is to send through to mortals, as we can, the knowledge of what war means on this plane—the plane all must face when they leave Earth life. By this means we hope to aid in keeping world peace."

This then was the meaning of all he had seen of those Masters and instructors; they were men who were trying to warn the politicians and the people of their danger. He might be of some small use in such a crusade; it would be an aim in this life that had so far made no impression upon him other than the feeling of its complete futility. He still longed for Carol and to be a part of her life; but if she was so encased in her materialist beliefs, it would be a waste of time.

However, he would try once more. Perhaps at home in the old surroundings he could find a way to reach her.

On landing, Carol went to the hospital and there arranged to take up her work when she should have finished her holiday at home.

Brainard was touched by her determination to make her life one of service to his unfortunate fellow soldiers. What other woman with her culture and fine nature would be able to carry on in such an atmosphere? Brainard was sure she was unique in her devotion to this ideal of service. He could only love her the more for it.

Yet how he wished he had been man enough to marry her when he had the chance and give her the life she was so well fitted for! What a mother she would have made for his children! What a home he could have made with her as the centre! Vain regrets now! It was all over for them until she should come to him. He would wait for her and they could, perhaps, find a way to be happy even in this wholly different sort of life.

He could wait, but he wanted her pledge.

CHAPTER XXXVI

✛

IN order to get to his home, Brainard knew he must still cling to Carol, as he was not yet able to transport himself. The most he could hope for was perhaps to make a contact with his own people that might impress Carol and comfort them. She could not dismiss his parents' testimony as she had Flanagan, the soldier who had written his message, and her own momentary sight of him.

The journey on the train was a dull one for both, though each was occupied with thoughts of the change that had come to them since they had last looked on this same flying landscape.

When they arrived, Carol was met by her father and mother and several old friends, all aglow with joy at her return. That she was changed they quickly saw, but only her mother betrayed it when she exclaimed:

"Carol, darling, you—you don't look the same."

"I'm not the same, Mother; you don't see what I have and not come away changed."

Of course they knew it was not all the war. It was Gordon's death too.

A silent witness to her homecoming was Brainard. He saw the way she fended off any reference to him. He knew she was not indifferent, yet he somehow wished he could hear her say she could not bear life without him. He was human enough to wish for that much.

As he drifted toward his home Brainard saw many faces that he knew. He paused in front of the shops on the main street and recalled his many visits to them from boyhood on.

When he came to the house that was *home* to him, he was a little shocked. There was a change; the lawn was neglected and so were his mother's plants on the veranda. He went inside, and there he felt a stranger. This closed-up, darkened place was not his home. He had never seen the shades drawn and the world shut out like this before.

He found his mother in her room upstairs, sitting aimless and idle in her chair. She who was always occupied, such a busy and competent housewife.

His father he discovered in his study with the evening paper but half unfolded, resting on his knee. How much greyer he had grown, and what a stoop had come to his shoulders! Presently he rose with the movements of an old man. At fifty-five to move like that!

These signs of their abiding grief and love were almost too much for him. If only he could tell them he was there with them!

Well, he must find a way.

To recover his poise he left his home and wandered about the town for some time. He met a few of the spirits of the old townspeople, souls rather primitive and unprogressive who were content to remain Earthbound in contact with their old home. They were just as he had always known them, simple, rather stupid and unambitious souls. He could find nothing in common with them now any more than he ever had.

The little home city gave Carol an enthusiastic welcome. All that the townspeople could contrive to show their appreciation of her service in France was done. Speeches, flowers, a dinner at which the Mayor presided, the newspapers' fulsome praise of her devotion to duty. There was his own picture at the head of the Roll of Honour in the courthouse. He was the one man killed among those conscripted from that locality.

Brainard was with Carol at all these affairs. He heard himself eulogized, and smiled at some of the exaggerations of his merits and descriptions of his military gallantry. Carol was not moved by them. She was too sane to take all that was said seriously. There had been too much oratory for any deep feeling to be aroused. The hardest moment for her had been when she looked at his photograph hung in the centre of the flag on the wall.

The Brainards had been invited, but they could not bring themselves to face such an ordeal. They were not resigned to the loss of their son, and Mrs. Brainard was not able to experience the exaltation that the mother of a fallen soldier is encouraged to feel when a gold star is given her as a decoration for her part in the work of overwhelming the enemy.

The daily visits of Carol were what meant most to them in these days. Like children they clung to her, for she was a link that somehow brought their son closer to them. They asked her question upon question about him. In answering, Carol tried to comfort them by uttering the platitudes that are invented for such situations, but she knew they were empty words. Their life had been dimmed and she could not light it up again for them.

All this Gordon saw and felt. He wanted now beyond all else to give his mother a sense of his presence, but when he tried to project his mind and break through to her consciousness he found he had so little force that he made no impression whatever. The events of his home-coming had been so fraught with sadness that it had a weakening effect on him. Now he cursed himself for throwing away his chance for the training that Morton and the instructors at Headquarters had offered him. Even Cummings had tried to show him the importance of making an effort. Now he knew that he could only help the ones he loved when he could command his mind.

The situation was unendurable. He longed to be away.

When the time came for Carol to go to her position in the hospital, Gordon was with her on the train, but he did not again try to make his presence felt.

Carol congratulated herself that the rest at home had completely restored her. Ahead lay her work. There would be plenty to occupy her and in some way she would be helping to make a life for those poor men in her care. On the days off, there would be plenty to see and hear. She was thankful that there had been no more hallucinations and uncanny ideas about Gordon, even at home, where the old scenes might have made them more vivid than ever. She would always adore his memory and feel that her personal life had stopped with his, but she must not give way to sentimentality and ruin her health and her capacity for useful work by letting herself go to pieces. There was still a world filled with beauty and art and she would enjoy them, taking each day as it came.

Carol had been a good and true lover, but her modern code was one of spiritual as well as physical and mental efficiency. No waste, no useless expenditure of feeling. She would live a life of service, and when its end came, there would be eternal forgetfulness. She had been shattered in the first hours of her loss, but now she would not repine, for that would change nothing. Gordon was for ever extinct and she would be also when her hour struck.

He got her thoughts. What a mild love hers was now! Just a memory daily receding into the distance. He wondered when it would be forgotten.

CHAPTER XXXVII

❖

THERE was no more interested student of Etheric life than Dent Cummings. He was so keen that his instructors made every effort to help him. The Master, Morton, now taking up his old task after the return journey from his war work in France, saw in Cummings the making of a brilliant and valuable addition to the company of souls who could attain to the heights of achievement. He thought Cummings the best man of all he had met among the war dead; for not only did he have a good background but he was a man of high spiritual quality. Not that Cummings was particularly religious; he was quite indifferent to the tenets of the various faiths. What he possessed, in marked degree, was the sense of moral responsibility and, with it, a faith in the purposes of life itself.

Cummings had made such progress in the power to transport himself that he was equal to most of his instructors in that respect. Also he could create beautiful objects. There was little purpose in his attempting to create a home, for there was no one to share it with. He was content to live in the one which his father had created and where his parents now lived. This was a duplicate of their house in the upper part of a main avenue in New York where he had lived as a boy. He was amazed to find his father's study and his mother's sitting-room replicas of the ones he remembered in their old home. The main reception room had been reproduced and the hall. There were, of course, no servants' rooms and no need of the dining-room or kitchen. There could be no use made of the many books he saw lining his father's study walls. These, like everything else, were only an appearance of the original shelves and their rows of volumes as his father remembered them. To a book-lover, the semblance of the works of favourite authors gives pleasure and keeps alive the memory of their contents.

The same paintings, seemingly, were on the walls of other rooms. All was as he had known it when he was growing up.

His mother was the feminine counterpart of himself; tall, with a dark beauty that was now at its zenith, for she had been able to discard the sense of middle age and was like a woman of thirty-five. This was true of his father. The three seemed to be of one generation.

The best of Cummings's life now was the knowledge that he was master of his own movements. He came and went wherever he willed. Always a traveller, he was now able to revisit the places he had been fond of and remembered distinctly. When the Masters saw how easily he could command his thought he became at once a centre of interest to them. They gave him a great deal of their attention, so that he was able to learn in a few months what it takes the average soul many years to master. He enjoyed most the hours he spent at the many concert auditoriums, buildings of surpassing beauty. There were fine programs of the best music; this was made by the musicians who could *think* the tones of their instruments and who remembered their scores. Glorious voices sang in chorus. The soloists were artists whose names were famous in their lifetime. There were magnificent galleries for paintings. These were either reproductions of the famous works of masters, or the mental creations of original ideas. There were noble conceptions by those who had never been painters in Earth life but whose love for the beautiful found expression in Etheric creation.

There was no need of shops, for all fashioned their own apparel mentally as they desired it. Often this led to rather an amusing ensemble. Some souls, long resident on the Etheric plane, dressed in the costumes they had known in mortal life. There were even those who garbed themselves as in the old colonial days. Others modelled their attire on that of the newly arrived souls. The women especially seemed to wish to be in the modern mode.

There were the great assembly halls and lecture rooms where distinguished minds, in all branches of knowledge, gave their addresses on the subjects of which they were masters. Many in their audiences were people who, in Earth life, had had little schooling and now were acquiring the education they had been denied. There were classes in the sciences. All was done without books or charts, pencils or paper. The mind was the only medium, but there were degrees given and titles bestowed, as in the Earthly universities.

The happiest places Cummings visited were the homes of the children. The souls of these small beings were cared for by women. Each had in her charge not more than twelve. They were taught to look upon her as their mother and to give her that title. As all service is voluntary, no woman took upon herself the task who was not inspired by a strong maternal feeling. Most of these women had been without children in their mortal life and they found in this work a free expression of their deepest instinct.

The children's homes were all of a different pattern and no institutional effect was to be seen. It was explained that these small creatures adapt themselves to their new existence very early and forget their brief life on Earth. After the third year the boys are taken to a "father." Usually the "father" is a young man who has himself been trained and grown up on the Etheric plane. He is free of most of the harsher traits that seem to be developed in a man who lives his full mortal span. The boys are taught to assume responsibility, to be loyal, fair, and truthful; and they are made to conform to rules of conduct.

There were so many new things to see and to learn, so much to think upon—the whole scheme of existence to survey from this new vantage—that for months Cummings was mentally occupied and even found this life a satisfying one.

It was only after the new technique of existence had been mastered that he felt the need of love. Not the love of friends, of parents —he had that—but the deeper need, the love of a woman. When the longing to see Doris, to hear her voice, and to still the searing pain of separation came upon him, he would make the focus of his thoughts her reception room. Sooner or later she would be there and he would make the most of the brief time near her.

When these short visits were over he felt a longing to let her know that he had been there. He was not so vain as to think she was unhappy, but he knew that she was not so gay as she used to be; less vivacious, and not so interested in the small talk of the friends she entertained. Her life was like a still pool; no turbulence and no disastrous surges, but still and quiet, with the deeps unstirred.

He knew very well that there was nothing to be gained by these visits. He often determined to be courageous enough to make an end to them. Yet there was a strong and overpowering longing to let her know that he was *living.*

What if he could find someone, someone like Flanagan, who could see and hear him! Then he could send her a message that would let her know that he was still alive; and after that some word that he loved her. He wanted her above all to know that.

CHAPTER XXXVIII

❖

POTTER was a very tractable man when he was asleep. Awake, he was the terror of the students. All had to be students in order to have a life that was not either dependent on the mental charity of others or a stationary existence.

Potter had been awakened by those in charge. Refreshed and invigorated by his long sleep, he was now ready to take up his life in "Heaven." He was in his element. All his life he had prepared for this. He had no inhibitions now; all his timidity, his doubt of himself, had vanished with his body. He had made a pact with God and was now prepared to keep it. Those in charge had been obliged to put him to sleep, with a few others of his kind, in order to make headway in their work with the rest of the soldiers. They hoped that when he awakened he might show a different spirit. They didn't know their man.

Potter looked upon all the instructors and Masters as demons, the slaves of the Devil of his theology, to be overcome by *him*, the militant son of righteousness. He paid no attention to their helpful instruction. He would not even listen. He considered their advice and explanations of the use of life in this realm as snares of Satan. He set his very stubborn will against all that he heard.

The other students were amused at his bigotry and rather enjoyed his outbursts. There were perhaps a hundred, more or less, like him, men from backward rural districts.

Potter was not very prepossessing; his tall bony figure looked a bit ridiculous in his soldier's uniform. As it was the dress he wore at his death, he carried over the impression of it as his present costume. When he was not closing his eyes to what the instructors showed him in the way of creating images by his thought-force, he was on his feet protesting, while his like-minded fellow students cheered and intoxicated him with the sense of his superiority over the Masters.

"You are the damned and this is the Hell prepared for you. Oh, you poor lost sheep!"—"sheep" meaning the soldiers who were attentive to the teaching.

"You are listening to the voices of *demons*. These men are trying to make you worship your own mind. They tell you to *create*. What blasphemy! There is but one Creator, the Lord God Almighty."

At this point the Master would interrupt:

"Of course, but we cannot know God except as we see His spark in the soul of man, His creation."

"That is blasphemy," Potter would roar. "Who says he cannot know God is already damned. I am here to warn you, my comrades, that unless you turn from these sons of Baal, you will *never* see God. You will burn with everlasting fire in the sea of flame that is the place of torment for all who bargain with the powers of darkness."

At this stage Potter would collapse with the force of his emotions and have to be put to sleep for a time so that the lecture could proceed. His followers would surround him and make their prayers to be led out of this hell into the Promised Land.

The Master who might be lecturing, Morton or another, would say:

"What can be done with such people? We have millions of others like them on this plane; some have been here for a century or more, still waiting to sit on the right hand of their Deity and rejoice in the thought that those who do not share their ideas are in torment. These people and their like are the most backward of any souls who come. Even the criminal and the sensualist *may* progress to a higher plane in time; but these cases are hopeless because they will not accept any scientific explanation of life."

Potter had an object in getting into the presence of the Almighty, apart from receiving the favours his Deity was waiting to shower upon him. *He was going to intercede for his beloved.* She must be saved and he was willing to take on the task. He wished to be made her guardian angel; then he could protect her from all the dangers of her present life—dangers peculiar to motion-picture stars as beautiful as she.

The delay in putting this plan before his Deity was maddening to him and he felt he must use all his power now and overthrow the enemies who were between him and the Lord of hosts.

There was a great outcry from his followers when he was again put to sleep. There was no arguing with them, no use telling them that he had been using up his mental power in his violent speeches and needed to recuperate, just as sleep is required by mortals to restore a physical body after exhausting manual labour.

Morton was the Master who had the soldier dead in charge. He had never been killed in battle, but he had seen every war the United States had waged, for he had been on the Etheric plane for more than three hundred years. He knew what war meant, for his had been the task of receiving young souls thrust from their bodies before they had really begun to live the life for which they had incarnated. Always keen to get back to Earth life, these youths had

been difficult problems. The idea of having to wait and to prepare
for another life irked them. They were impatient to start again, to
get into a body and try once more. These lads of the A.E.F. were the
most difficult of all, for they had been given little or no spiritual
instruction. They felt that life was only the span between birth and
death; and so to have a merry time and make a success of their
careers was all they expected. There was no sound foundation laid
in their public or private education that prepared them for a life
after death. The few from families who had given them the benefit
of religious instruction were almost equally ignorant of their destiny. The doctrine of immortality had been taught them, but no
explanation had been given them of what it was. They now had to
be taught that the *mind* is the immortal part of mankind, and in the
mind the *soul,* or *divine spark* that is *life itself,* resides.

They were, of course, disappointed to find that it was up to them
to make progress just as it had been in mortal life. They had to
accept the fact that all is cause and effect on every plane of existence; that no great intelligence is needed to master the few principles of Etheric life, though success or failure depends upon the
strength of will; also that degrading practices in the Earthly span
weaken the will and make for defeat in the after life.

These were simple things to grasp and all are clearly set forth
in the scriptures of many religions; yet they have become so over-
laid with ancient taboos, superstitions, and the teachings en-
gendered by greed for power in the different sects that they seem
to be lost.

The preachment of Morton was one of constructive evolution:
always the mind leading the individual forward whether on Earth
or on the Etheric plane, with faith in the Law of Life.

"We are all on our path and each where he belongs. Do not blame the Deity for your failures. You are the result of all you have been. Man cannot die. As soon as he understands that, he may learn how to live. There are planes beyond this, as a few of you know who have delved into the study of occult lore; but here, on *this* plane, is where you decide your own future. *Here* is where every soul must come when the breath stops and his Etheric body is freed. Any promise or belief that you can beat the game and skip this plane will have to be abandoned. You can learn to conquer life here by self-mastery *only*. There are three courses open to you:

"You can drift and lead a life of complete idleness.

"You can learn to control your mind to a point where you can reincarnate and go into a body of flesh, to live another mortal life.

"Or you can study, improve yourself, and, when you are weary of this plane, be shown how to ascend to a higher vibratory realm which we know as the Spiritual plane. All is serene there. They have no weak moronic mentalities to deal with there, no children to care for, and no war dead to receive.

"Here there are a few of us who could go on to that peaceful plane if we would, but we dedicate ourselves to the task of helping the helpless. We are glad to do this so long as our strength is equal to the task. Your politicians and war-creators are making this all but impossible. We have only so much mind-power to give out in the way of help. If your men of Earth continue to slaughter millions of youth and send them here before their time, we shall not be able to cope with the tragedy. To save ourselves we shall have to abandon our labours here and go on to the Spiritual plane for self-preservation.

"This realm was once the 'Hell,' the 'Sheol,' referred to by the ancient writers. Seers and oracles with Etheric vision reported it as the place of lost souls; and indeed that very well described it. As

modern thought freed itself from old and terrible shackles of superstitions, souls came here who devoted themselves to bringing light
and leadership, order and the scientific spirit. To them we owe a
debt that can never be estimated. This plane is now organized, orderly, and progressive. Those unable to rise above their animal instincts are held in check. Souls here are in the van of mental and
spiritual progress. As with you on Earth, so here, the few bear the
burden and lead the many. But now we have come to the most critical time in many centuries. Not only are you turning science into
an engine of destruction for those of Earth, but you are making this
plane a Hell again. Your war victims in our hospitals which you
have not seen because we wish to spare you—these men came over
with minds so shattered by their last horrible impressions of the
carnage that it has wiped out all previous memories. They relive,
over and over again, the horrors of their last hours, and because of
the power of their thoughts they reproduce in the ether the frightful
ful scenes that they cannot forget. What do we do for them? We
try to dominate their minds and give them the blessing of oblivion,
of forgetfulness, of sleep for a few hours. If only the men who prate
so glibly of their new methods for mass murder in war were made
to see these men, to see the scenes of slaughter their tortured minds
have created, perhaps they would dread their own fate when they
must come to share the horrors they are responsible for. We, who
deal with the wreckage of war on this plane, have no illusions.
Human character has been on the wane for fifty years. Greed, love
of power, a cynical attitude toward the love of men and women, the
weakening of moral fibre, and the effort to find an easy way out of
every problem, have made Americans a far different people from
their forebears. *Here we get you as you are.* I have known and taught
seven generations of my people here. I have no illusions. And yet

I am not without hope though I face the truth that we have failed in our high mission as a nation dedicated to the task of bringing in an era of enlightenment and progress. We have now tossed it aside to become involved in the Old World hatreds and conflicts that the men who built the Republic left their native lands to avoid. You are young; your incarnation was cut short by this war. You are keen to return. *For what? Do you know?* Here, if you will stay and work with us, we can assure you of a life of usefulness. You will not have the pleasures the senses can give, but there are others, of the spirit, that you will find can make life very happy. We cannot *ask* you to deny yourselves for the sake of the race. We can only say *some must serve,* and we believe that you will find the service worth your sacrifice."

CHAPTER XXXIX

❖

THERE were few of his audience who could believe what Morton told them. *They* had been able to withstand the shock of death in battle; why shouldn't the rest of their comrades? They were inclined to be cynical and think the Masters were "faking" in order to get them to stay and share the work of teaching. Each man decided that he was not going to help anyone but *himself*. Each had been regimented until he was in the mood to cast off every bond and live for himself alone.

Cummings was in the small minority who accepted all that was put before them as the simple truth. Many of the students went so far as to laugh and make a joke of the idea that men could be insane after death.

Morton answered this outburst.

"What are you so amused about? Perhaps you think we are telling you an untruth. You will be shown just what we have described."

The teachers then, in mass concentration, transported the scoffers to the places where their unfortunate comrades were being cared for.

When the students had been returned, they were silent and with a different expression entirely. They had the apearance of men who had looked into Hell.

"You have seen the poor fellows I have asked you to help. You now know what war really can mean here. You may choose to try to forget them, yet you will find that you cannot do so. The things you have just seen are not to be forgotten by a mind that is above that of a fool. You can abandon these poor sufferers or you can help them. They will require a century or more to regain the mental control that will make them normal again, but now is the time that they most need us all. We older spirits cannot hold out much longer without help. The mortal plane could do much. Every town, city, or village that has lost some of its youth in this war could, by mass thought centred on them, bring some peace to these souls who are unable to forget and are still living over their last terrible moments. The speeches, the white crosses, the monuments that will be raised, can do nothing for them. And you, after what you have seen, can you young souls face living again in a world dedicated to war? Will you be willing to risk your body and mind in a civilization that will use you as a cog in a machine for conquest? What will you gain by reincarnating in such a world? Face these questions squarely before you decide on your future."

The men were now silent; they were no longer able to joke or even to smile. There were no more sneers at the teachers and no more gibes at the Masters. They were appalled at what they had seen.

There was one who was unmoved by all this—Potter. He had no hesitation in saying that the war was the wrath of God punishing the world until it turned from its sins. His attitude of self-righteousness was in such contrast to that of the others that he was even bereft of his followers. Human brotherhood had triumphed over bigotry and superstition.

There was one who was silent, yet always attentive—Dent Cummings. He grasped the principle underlying all that he saw and heard. It was clear to him that the whole race was doomed unless on the Earth plane men began to understand the facts of life in the Etheric plane. What could rouse them? The old Bible quotation came to him that "they would not believe though one rose from the dead." He knew this was true. Man had worshipped himself until he was incapable of faith in anything else. Man could no longer rise to a point of understanding the realm outside his physical senses.

All that Cummings could think of, notwithstanding this, was how to tell the mortal world of its danger. Never inclined to mix with a miscellaneous company, he was now more than ever alone. His parents were occupied with their social rounds and were not interested in the problems of the soldiers or in anything but themselves and their own group of friends. What had become of the old American spirit of loyalty and neighbourliness? When he questioned his father, the answer was:

"We had no part in making this war. We are not concerned with the things of the world any longer. When you are well adjusted here, your mother and I intend to ascend to the Spiritual plane. We are done with Earth life for ever. The peace and quiet of life in the higher realms, and the company of each other, are all we ask."

Cummings was shocked. Could anything be more selfish and brutal? *They* were comfortable and could betake themselves where they would not be conscious of the many cruel problems left by the World War.

He was more than ever lonely, more thoughtful; and in the hours of mental solitude his mind turned to Doris. What would she think of all this, he wondered. He finally asked Morton if there was any way that he could get a message through to a friend. The Master answered:

"A few people among mortals can either see us or hear our voices; still fewer can do both; but these channels of communication are usually choked by the hordes of friends and relatives who merely wish to exchange greetings and assure their families that all is well with them here. This makes it impossible to find a medium that can be used by us for useful information. In any case, the public mind is so prejudiced against clairvoyance and clairaudience that we have given up hope of making a dent in the hard materialism of the American mind. Europe is far in advance of us in these matters."

After a moment's thought he added:

"There is such a man whom I have seen recently on one of my tours of inspection. This chap had remarkably clear Etheric vision and hearing. An ex-soldier and a cripple. I believe his name is Flanagan. Another soldier called him by that name."

Cummings was startled. Why, of course, it *would* be Flanagan!

Morton recounted his experience in a motion-picture theatre. When Cummings expressed surprise that he should visit such a place, he answered:

"We make a tour of inspection regularly. We look in on your stage, screen, dance halls, your night clubs and beach resorts. We look at the display of magazines, newspapers, and books. We listen to your radio broadcasts. How else can we judge of the influences that are moulding the minds of those who will eventually come to us here? We are quite aware of the commercialized degradation that passes for amusement in our country these days. Even music, painting, and sculpture are mediums for the obscenities that pass as modern art. We have no other way of understanding the souls of those we must try to humanize. You have not been corrupted by these trends; you have had the strength to withstand the tide of mental sewage that has engulfed the average youth of your time."

Cummings was amazed at the scorn and contempt that the Master took no pains to conceal. Morton smiled at Cummings's look of surprise.

"We are not gods. We are men, with all the feelings and passions of men. We strive to control our emotions, as we do our thoughts, but we are too human to bear with indifference the modern craze to banish beauty, grace, and charm from the world. The wits and so-called 'intelligentsia' are even levelling their shafts at love, the one thing that can redeem the race. All is sexualism and morbidity in the circles where the 'sophisticates' prevail. We cannot make any pretence to tolerance for these exhibitions of moral decadence. We know there are people who still make a stand for decency and beauty, but they are silenced by the clamour of the corrupted masses. Well, we shall not accept the mob standard. Here we try to salvage the souls of those who are worth saving. As *all* are worth saving, we put the best before them, and if they choose the worst we can only let them go their way."

Cummings was not surprised at these comments. He had turned from the cult of ugliness that was creeping over the culture of the Western world.

What could he do now? How help to stay the tide?

To speak the truth to the world! If there could only be a way found to do this, perhaps the enlightened few would seize upon it and blazon it to the rest of the people.

Yet it all seemed so chimerical—so fantastic!

Still, he could not give up the idea and clung to one point as a starter—*Flanagan.*

CHAPTER XL

⁂

THE best of times was when Molly was at home all day on Sunday. She would spend part of the day in darning and mending after they had come from mass. They had agreed to forget the world on Sunday and make it a day of rest—rest in the sense of ignoring Flanagan's quest for employment, as well as Molly's office grind.

They had little to be happy with: a small room with a rear outlook in a cheap neighbourhood; but the place was kept in perfect order and Molly had the knack of making it attractive with a few of her possessions.

The two were so sure of each other that they were content. Whatever the future offered in the way of a challenge, they were sure they could meet it. When they had been together as man and wife for a few weeks, the naturalness and perfection of their union made them sure they were divinely mated. This acted to give them a greater faith in life and made them fearless of the future.

Such simple pleasures as a walk in the Park or a visit to the museum they made the most of. They were fond of riding on the buses up to the end of the city. They had no money for amusements, but somehow they found plenty to see, to admire, to wonder at, and to discuss. The daily newspaper supplied them with a record of the events of the world, and Flanagan loved to follow the sports. The weather was still too cold for loitering and they found their room a cozy refuge after the chill of the streets.

Occasionally they made a pilgrimage to the Cathedral and there knelt together and gave thanks for the gift of their happiness.

Flanagan was now getting stronger and cleverer with his crutch. Once while he was searching for the employment that he was determined to run down, he stopped for a moment on a corner to verify the address he was looking for and, to his astonishment, heard his name spoken. He looked about him and decided that he had been mistaken. Suddenly, directly in front of him, he saw the figure of Hanson looming.

He had been careful to shut out all sounds and sights that were not of Earth life ever since his experience with Cummings on the boat coming home, when he was aware of many spirits of dead American soldiers, as well as other figures whose presence he could not account for, as they were not in the A.E.F. uniform. He was no stranger to Hanson's spirit, for on the crossing from France Hanson was a loud-mouthed pest to both Flanagan and the dead.

Now here he was again! Flanagan was not going to hold any communication with him and so did not respond to his name. The impression he got was that Hanson was more repulsive than ever.

He went on and into the building he was seeking, but Hanson was beside him. He was tempted to turn back, then decided to go on and make his application. This was for a bookkeeping job, for he had been studying for that work lately. When he got into the elevator Hanson was beside him still and was seemingly amused at the way he managed his crutch.

"You got a nifty third leg there, my lad! I didn't have your luck. The Goddam Heinies got me fer good."

As he got out of the elevator and went into the office he sought, still Hanson was with him and heard the interview that followed.

When he reached the street again, there was Hanson leering and saying:

"Looking for a job! Well, I'm damned! Where's your Uncle Sam?"

Flanagan knew that Molly would be waiting for him in a little while at the place uptown where they went for their inexpensive dinners, and he wondered how he could rid himself of this presence. He made a feint of going into a tobacco shop as if to make a purchase. Hanson was alongside him, saying:

"I wish I was in that body of yours and could light a cigarette. Now with Rosenberg all I get is the eats. I want a smoke."

Flanagan left the shop before the clerk could wait on him. He was now realizing that Hanson could not be shaken off. He turned a corner finally and leaned up against the side wall of the building. Hanson stood facing him and was all but on top of him. He now recalled how he had been able to speak to Brainard and Cummings by simply thinking the words clearly and slowly. He tried it now.

"Look here, Hanson, you've bothered me long enough. What do you want?"

"Well, by God, he can see me! Say, Flanagan, you see me, don't you?"

"Yes, and I can hear you. What do you want with me?"

"I just wanted to be sociable. This spirit life ain't my style. I want a body. That's what I want, and the fun I used to have before I went into this damned spirit life."

"I can't do anything about it. I want you to leave me alone now."

"Oh, hell! Be a pal. Let's go where the fun is."

Flanagan was near his wits' end. He was not aware of the method by which a spirit can take possession of a mortal, but he had heard of obsession by low spirits and he gathered that Rosenberg was Hanson's victim. He knew the insane asylums were filled with patients who were invaded by degraded mentalities and he feared this haunting presence.

He dared not go to meet Molly with this wretch hanging to him. When they had walked a short way again, Hanson said:

"Where are you going? Come on, let's go to a show."

Flanagan realized that perhaps he could rid himself of Hanson by going to a picture theatre. He watched for one and, buying a ticket, was about to go in when Hanson called out to him:

"Look who's here! One of the Masters taking in a show!"

Flanagan recognized the spirit of a man that Hanson was looking at as one he himself had seen on the boat. He was going into the theatre ahead of them. Flanagan wondered about this. If a spirit such as this was attending a theatre, it must be that life after death was not so different from the one he was living.

When they got inside, this spirit was standing in the centre of the auditorium between the seats and looking at the screen, though apparently not obscuring it from the people behind him. Flanagan marvelled at this.

The Master saw Hanson and recognized him, but apparently he was not pleased at the sight. Hanson was too intent on watching the picture to observe this. Morton, for it was that Master, was soon beside them, saying to Hanson in a very stern tone:

"This is the last place I expected to find you, Hanson. I hear you are making the waterfront dives your hangout."

Hanson was not in the least abashed.

"Oh, I like a change. This lame fellow here is one of my old outfit."

Morton looked at Flanagan and then at Hanson as if he was sure the little cripple was not of the same stripe.

"Is he aware of you?"

"Oh, he can see me and I can talk to him. He hears me all right."

Morton then turned to Flanagan.

"Are you clairvoyant? Can you see me?"

"Yes. Won't you get this fellow to leave me alone?" He answered silently.

"Is he forcing himself on you?"

"Yes, I can't get rid of him."

"Oh, come now! I jest wanted to be a pal," Hanson put in.

Morton turned to Hanson. "You are making yourself a nuisance. Why don't you let him alone?"

"I want to find a new pal. Flanagan used to be in my outfit. I guess I got a right to be with an old buddy."

The face of Morton was stern as he turned to Flanagan. "This man is Earthbound. He may do you harm if you encourage his presence."

"I don't want him around me. He was no buddy of mine. I want him to leave me alone."

Flanagan said this in his thought and tried to make it emphatic. The master spirit answered:

"Leave this place at once, then, and go to your home. He will not be able to follow you while I am here to control him with my will."

The way to the eating place was quite a distance, and when Flanagan got there Molly was becoming alarmed. He was preoccupied during the meal and she wondered what could have happened. When they were alone in their room, he said suddenly:

"Molly, if I tell you something that sounds queer you won't think I'm off my head?"

"What a question! Of course not."

He then told her of his experience that afternoon. Molly listened with growing terror. She was sure he was losing his mind. Still she managed to keep her self-control.

"You just imagined it, dear."

"No. I've always been able to see and hear the spirits, though this is the first time I've told anybody."

Then he told her about Brainard and Cummings and how they had talked with him after they had been killed.

Molly was all but paralysed with fear. Her man was going crazy. What ought she to do? She must have help for him before it was too late.

Flanagan saw the fear in her face and he tried to explain that it was nothing to be alarmed about; many people could see and hear the spirits. Look at all the mediums and the Spiritualists who make a religion of it. He tried to show her that the Bible was filled with stories of such things.

The more he talked, the more Molly felt that his mind was going. She scarcely took in what he was saying. She tried to persuade him to stop talking and go to bed and rest. She was not quite the same with him—just as sweet and loving, but she seemed to be holding something back in her mind.

The rest of the night he lay wondering about his strange experience. Evidently the second spirit was a superior one and could control Hanson. Then he remembered what Cummings had proposed and how he had refused to listen when Cummings had said: "If people were only sure that we soldiers go on living and remembering, it might make them afraid to keep on killing us in wars."

What if it were true and the newspapers would print things that came through that way!

What if it were true that people would read such things and he could do his bit as Cummings suggested!

What if he could save other men from the hell he'd been through!

What if he could *make war on war* just by telling the simple truth!

The idea began to possess him.

CHAPTER XLI

❖

THE most poignant moment in Flanagan's life was when he realized that Molly thought him not in his right mind and that she had plotted with the doctor to examine him. Of course he had not been feeling very well; his nerves were on edge because of his failure to find work, and on the ground of this nervous condition he had yielded to Mollie and gone with her to see the doctor.

This was a celebrated and much advertised specialist in mental diseases and with the best practice in this class of cases of anyone in the city. Molly's employer had recommended him after he had heard her story, as he was a kindly man and valued Molly's faithfulness even more than her ability, which was no more than average, yet sufficient to the demands made upon it.

The doctor decided, as his questioning proceeded, that this was not the most amiable patient in the world. Flanagan was in a rage when he discovered what he had been tricked into. Molly really believed then that he was "nutty."

What a fool he had been to tell her of his seeing and hearing the spirits! She was so devoted that here she was making a sacrifice too heavy for her slim purse in order to do what she thought was best for him. He was uncertain what he should say or do.

He thought, if the doctor was a man who understood, he would tell Molly the truth, that her husband simply had an extra power of sight and hearing. Everything would be all right then, and Molly would have to believe. If not—anything could happen.

Flanagan was in an agony of suspense, and so was Molly. After the questioning was over, Flanagan said:

"Look here, doctor, you know there are such things as seeing and hearing spirits."

The doctor was coldly emphatic:

"I have never seen or heard a spirit, my dear young friend, and, what is more, no one else has. These are hallucinations and they should be cured. Otherwise you run a terrible risk of having them grow upon you until they upset your mental balance."

Flanagan saw that he was not going to make this man confess to the facts. When they left the doctor's office he was silent and Molly was in the mood to suggest a diversion by dropping into their local picture theatre. Flanagan was too concerned and worried to raise any objections.

They were about to enter the place when Flanagan saw the figure of Dent Cummings standing on the curb watching the passers-by. As soon as they came near, he smiled and joined them.

"Hello, Flanagan! This is lucky. I've been hoping to find you and this was my lookout post."

Flanagan paid no attention to him, determined to shut off all this sort of thing.

Cummings was amazed that he had apparently not been heard, remembering how easily Flanagan and he had conversed on the ship; so he stood close to Flanagan while Molly purchased the tickets. Cummings began to explain why he was trying to get co-operation and what his object was. By this time they had all three gone into the theatre. Flanagan, when he saw that Cummings was going to persist until he got a response, said mentally:

"For God's sake, let me alone. I'm not going to listen or have anything to do with spirits."

Cummings was not to be put off, thinking this simply one of Flanagan's cranky moods.

"There isn't the least danger. I'll have the best Masters on this plane taking care of you. This is a thing that is too important to be passed up. You can be the greatest benefactor in the whole world if you will work with me."

"Like hell I will! I tell you to leave me alone and get your benefactor somewhere else."

Cummings saw there was no use in further argument; he left the theatre but waited outside. When the two came out, he followed at a distance. Molly was chatting and seemed now to be all animation, but Flanagan was moody and scarcely answered when she spoke to him.

Later, in the room, when Molly was getting an impromtu dinner, Flanagan said:

"Molly, I guess you think I'm going nutty and you made me go with you to that doctor to have him cure me. That right?"

Molly was evasive.

"Oh, I thought your nerves were bad and you were beginning to imagine things. You know you've had a hard time and it's no wonder if you have a nervous breakdown."

"That's what they call it, is it? Well, I'm not going to have any, so don't run up any more bills for it."

"Now, honey, don't you fret about the bills."

"When did you decide that I was nervous and needed a doctor?"

Molly was confused and didn't answer very clearly.

"Why, you've been ever so nervous for over a month now."

"Yes, but I know what the doctor said to me. You were in the outside room. I know why you made me go to him. Let's forget it now. Let's never speak of it again. Promise?"

"Of course, dear."

She had her arms around him and her cheek against his. She felt happy again. She was sure the doctor must have cured him already.

Flanagan was now determined to keep the spirits of his old comrades at a distance.

Then followed the most desperate and discouraging time. Flanagan began to see that he was really beaten. He did not speak of it to Molly, but he admitted it to himself. She was the support of both and had no money to spare now for the many little items she needed to keep herself looking fresh and pretty. The change in her appearance was noted in the office and the other girls were not slow in commenting on it, hoping to receive favourable comparison from their employer.

When the hot months came Molly realized that she was pregnant and the period when she would be able to work would soon be over.

She did not tell Flanagan because she feared what he might do in his desperation. He was rapidly sinking into a state of hopelessness.

She herself had also given up faith, and the future was so terrifying she dared not think of it.

CHAPTER XLII

✤

A SMALL, but sharp pain had been stabbing Molly all day; she had felt the most sickening weakness after it, but had gone on and tried to ignore it as she worked away at the letters her employer had dictated. When the time came to leave the office, she was too ill to trust herself to the crowds on the street and in the subway. She waited until the others had left the office, then made her way to the street very slowly and carefully. She went to the near-by drug store and asked to be given something to stop the pain. A small dose of a powerful drug was given her and she started for home.

Flanagan was in the room preparing their meagre dinner. As Molly came in, her white and drawn face showed the pain she was suffering. Flanagan was terrified. He thought perhaps she needed food and tried to persuade her to eat something, but Molly only wanted to lie down, to sleep and forget the pain. Flanagan managed to make her ready for bed and helped her into it, but she had scarcely fallen asleep before she was crying out with pain. . . .

At the hospital they told Flanagan that there was no way of preventing the premature birth; that his wife was too weak to be a mother.

Then there was the slow work of regaining strength. Molly sat up in the ward bed and thought over the future. What could her husband do? She knew now that she was not equal to supporting them both.

Her courage had waned.

Her child, *theirs*, the bond that was to such a joy to both of them, was never to be.

What was it that made them the most unlucky couple in New York?

Thinking it over, she was sure that it must be their lost faith in God. They had not been to the priest and they had not tried to make their life truly religious. Only that could be the reason why she and her husband were not allowed the comfort and happiness most couples enjoyed.

When Flanagan came to see her he sat holding her hand, with his heart in his eyes. He could say nothing that would be of help. He was so miserable over the failure of all their hopes that he spoke only in answer to her questions. One thing he decided in his own mind: she was not going back to work; he would be firm on that point. Molly was still too weak to do more than smile and tell him not to be foolish.

Flanagan was now more than ever determined to make a place for himself somehow, somewhere.

He had been in a strange state of dumb despair for months, but Molly's illness had acted as a shock that made him alive to the situation. He saw that he must take the burden from now on. Molly must give up all idea of office work and he must make the living. How he would do it he did not know, but if there was a God He would answer his plea for work now.

He went from the hospital to the Cathedral. There, where he and Molly had made their prayers, he knelt and with desperate faith in the power of Divinity to give him succour, he made his petition to Almighty God.

When he had finished, he raised his eyes and saw, in the dim beauty of the vaulted church, a most heavenly light. It came from a soul standing near the altar. The man that stood within its encircling radiance was not the priest but a being that wore a blue robe. A young and vigorous figure it was, with a face both strong and compassionate.

When Flanagan realized that this was simply a human spirit and not an angel or a divine messenger, his heart was sick, for he had somehow looked for a miracle in answer to his prayer.

The figure moved toward him and seemed to wish to speak to him.

Flanagan was terrified. Could it be that he was not secure when he was in church? Did the dead walk even in the aisles of the house of God?

A voice spoke that was gentle and friendly:

"I heard your prayer, my poor friend, and I wish I might aid in bringing its answer."

Flanagan was too broken now to be combative, but he was silent. The spirit spoke on:

"We are only humans and we come here also to pray and to meditate. These beautiful silent houses of worship can lift the soul to higher levels and bring it near to the source of its being."

The sweep of these thoughts Flanagan was not fully able to grasp but a quieter feeling came over him.

So the spirits were still men and needed to pray even as he! That thought gave him a sense of fellowship with this one whose voice was more than a man's, for it had in it the note of authority, of power, and of profound understanding and pity.

Suddenly, as if a dam had burst, Flanagan began to weep.

His long and bitter battle to live, to work, to take his station in life as a man, to make a place for the woman he loved, he had lost.

All the months of humiliation and despair, the cruel realization that he was scrapped like a piece of worn-out armament, all this was in the sorrow that he could no longer master. The silent sobs shook his shoulders as he laid his head on his arms, and his tears were let to flow at last. Tears that scalded and burned and seared his face. He was like a child that has lost his way and finds the darkness coming on.

Then the voice of the stranger spirit again—now closer and with infinite tenderness:

"My poor lad, you have known all the tortures that man has made for man. You are one of the millions who have been robbed of their chance in life, your birthright. We, who receive the souls of the dead, are only too well aware of your hard fate. We have no power in the mortal world except as we can give to men the benefit of our experience and now and then, in some small degree, strengthen them and give them the courage to persist. We wish to serve all, to give what aid we can in time of need. Perhaps, in some small way, I can be of help to you."

Flanagan listened.

What was it he heard the voice saying? Help? Was there one in all the universe who offered help?

Only the spirit of a dead man.

CHAPTER XLIII

✣

"WHEN shall I see you again?" Flanagan's voice was now eager and hopeful.

"I shall be here each day at this hour. I am interested in what you can do to help us and also we hope to aid you. Wait here; I shall send Cummings to you."

Suddenly the light, and the figure within it, flashed out. Flanagan forgot his own plight in thinking over what he had just heard.

Morton had told him of the blind and suicidal course the race was taking, and the effort he and others were making to warn mortals of their danger. Not only was their future civilization at stake but their more important future in the realm they must inhabit after death. He described conditions on the Etheric plane; the congestion of souls through the war; the shattered minds of many of the victims. He made a point of the fact that there was only chaos ahead for future generations unless a change came over the spirit of the people.

Then he told him of Cummings's desire to use his knowledge of conditions on both planes and, by working with someone like Flanagan who had Etheric sight and hearing, to give the world a plan of co-operation. This in the hope of preventing war and also to promote progress and the spiritual understanding of his fellow countrymen.

Flanagan was in a state of mental exaltation. He had forgotten himself in listening to this one who spoke of far greater things than he could grasp. Somehow he felt lifted up, as though a great honour had been bestowed on him.

Surely he must be of some account for such a spirit to ask him to come in on a thing as big as this. It was wonderful!

Of course he would work with Cummings now that he understood.

Flanagan had been made whole again.

Outside the world was ready to trample him, but in this sanctuary he had been given a chance to serve in a truly great cause. He was part of a Crusade for Peace.

There had been a time when he would have called all this "bunk." He had believed that man loved war for its own sake. Well, only those who had never known war would say such a thing these days.

There were no witnesses to this strange interview. Those who entered to tarry for a few moments saw only a man kneeling silently and apparently lost in communion with God. The verger was somewhat puzzled that such a young man should be so devout. Then he decided that the fellow looked shabby and might be only seeking shelter and rest.

Flanagan's thoughts were interrupted by a new light coming toward him, not so bright as the other. It was Cummings.

He came to Flanagan and gave him a cheery greeting. Flanagan was struggling up on his crutch.

"No, no! Sit down, Flanagan, and be comfortable. I've just heard the good news."

Flanagan sat down and, with a flush that told more than his words, said mentally:

"I wasn't very decent to you, Cummings, but I didn't understand. I hope you won't hold it against me."

"In your place I should have done the same. Forget it. We are partners now. You can write down the things I shall tell you, just simply and plainly. Of course it's only a chance that we can make an impression on the mind of the public, or even on the minds of the editors and publishers; but it would be a crime not to make the attempt."

He thought of Doris. She could be a help in persuading Martin to publish the writings of Flanagan that he would direct. If only she would believe!

Morton had told him Flanagan's story. The thing was to find someone who could, and would, make the effort to help him and his wife. If Doris knew, of course, she would be glad to do all possible for them. Still he had no idea what her reaction would be to Flanagan. The time was precious and help must come at once if it was to be of any use. The most that he could expect of Doris was that she would grant an interview and read his message. He explained to Flanagan that the first move was to write a note to his friend Mrs. Martin Fuller, which he would dictate.

Side by side, as they had often marched over the muddy roads of France, they went down the Avenue. One visible, limping along on a crutch; the other unseen, erect, perfect, but only the image of a man.

They went over to Flanagan's room and there Cummings dictated his message.

Dear Doris:

You will be surprised to know that I am able to send you this message. We do not die, we only leave our bodies. I was with you in my room the day you called there and I know all that is in your heart. I was never able to tell you what was in mine. The bearer of this was in my outfit and was wounded during the engagement in which I was killed with two others of our unit. He is gifted with clairvoyance and clairaudience and is able to both see and hear me. This letter is in his handwriting. I hope you will aid him in getting clerical work. He is about to collaborate with me on a book describing this plane of existence. In the meantime his wife is in the hospital. You will, I know, do all possible to help them both for my sake. When you read this I shall be present and if you wish to question me through the bearer, he will be able to relay my replies. As you read this it is, perhaps, the supreme moment of our lives. You have the power to open the way for my work through Flanagan. On you rests a great responsibility. I know you will be equal to it, being what you are.

Dent

The way to the Fuller home was not far, and within an hour Flanagan was ringing the bell, with Cummings beside him.

CHAPTER XLIV

❖

DORIS FULLER said to the maid who announced Mr. James Flanagan:

"I don't know such a person."

"He says he has a letter for you that's important, madam."

"Where is it?"

"He said when I asked him for it that he must deliver it in person. He's a cripple, madam."

"I suppose it's a beggar."

"I should think likely, madam."

"Tell him I am not at home."

She was in the midst of a conversation with an author, one of her husband's most profitable writers; and they were discussing his next book.

The maid had gone as far as the door when Doris was conscious of a definite feeling that she was doing wrong. She had the sense of a presence beside her and the most poignant feeling of the importance of the moment.

"Wait!"

She had called out suddenly to the maid, who stopped at the door in surprise. Doris scarcely knew that she had said the word, it had been spoken on such a flashing impulse. Now she was embarrassed at her impetuous about-face and was ready to tell the maid to go on and dismiss the mendicant. Yet—

Again she felt a thrilling sense of one guiding her and, half in wonder at herself, she said to her guest:

"Perhaps I should see what this is all about. Since I've been doing war work all sorts of people make it a business to call on me. This might be a soldier on an errand from the Red Cross. If you don't mind I'll have him shown into the library. I shan't be long."

Flanagan saw Cummings follow the maid when she left to announce him, and now, as she returned and showed him into the book-lined room, there was Cummings beside a very smart and lovely lady.

"What is it you wish to see me about?"

"This letter explains it."

She took the letter and went to a window, her back turned to him as she opened it. She had been courteous but very casual and a little bored. She had scarcely read a line, however, when her whole manner changed. Her shoulders stiffened in eager interest, her head bent lower, and her hand trembled so that the letter shook.

Cummings was still beside her and from his expression Flanagan knew and understood the love that was flooding the woman as she read.

She paused for a moment in the midst of the reading and put her hand over her eyes. Then she seemed to pull herself together and go on.

Cummings was too fine to speak aloud his feelings before a third person and he made no attempt to touch her.

When she had finished reading the letter Doris stood silent and as though unable to grasp the full meaning of what was written there. She read it over again. Then, as though her mind had fully grasped all that lay in the words, she moved to the great carved table in the centre of the room and sank into the chair behind it. She sat with her hands clasped over the letter that lay before her.

Finally, with a glow in her eyes, she looked at Flanagan—a long look that was more than a look; it was a reading of the man's soul. His clear gaze met hers steadfastly. Then she spoke in a low tone:

"Bless you for this!"

Only four words, but they held the whole story of her love and her understanding.

In his own room that evening Flanagan for the first time was at peace with life. There was a sense of more than peace. He felt a joy and a release; a pure feeling of oneness with the laws of the universe. He could not have put into words these strange and profound convictions, but he was sure that at last he was on a path that he could safely follow.

What lay ahead ultimately he did not know, but there was the perfect faith in him that all would be well and that he would be a factor in the world; that world where yesterday he had felt himself one too many in the scheme of things, unwanted and betrayed.

Later Cummings came to him and they began their work together. A dozen pages were taken down in Flanagan's clear and finely formed writing. They were inspired by the things Morton had shown them and by the lessons already learned of the Science of Life.

When their work was done Flanagan was exhausted. He was not the man to complain, but he had a bruised feeling at the back of his head above the spine and to the right of it. Cummings explained that the gland situated there was the receiving station for his voice. This gland has such radio-active power that a spirit can use it.

Cummings said further that there was a certain amount of the medium's vitality consumed in this association. Also that the reason he could speak to him, and not to others, was because of the extra power that came like a light from his head.

Flanagan was not alarmed. Somehow he felt protected. He had known Cummings for a good sport, always giving way to the selfishness of Hanson and tolerantly putting up with Potter's and Rosenberg's peculiarities. Even the awful carnage did not seem to more than make him ill and nauseated. He never expressed hatred and had no violent outbursts as the others did. Yet he was the lily-handed highbrow of the outfit.

Cummings's friend, Mrs. Fuller, had insisted upon giving Flanagan an advance on the writing he was to do. That made the way clear for Molly. He had taken her the news in the hour set for visitors that evening before he began his work with Cummings. He dared not tell her what this writing was that he had found to do. He must be careful and never let her know the nature of it. He would wait until the book was published before he came out with all the facts.

Molly, of course, lay in a soft heaven of warm thankfulness and peace.

She had only to grow strong now.

CHAPTER XLV

❖

WHEN the book was finally published, the book that had cost so
many hours of painful and exhausting collaboration between
Flanagan and Cummings, the reviews of *Life on the Etheric* were
few and the reviewers inclined to speak of its revelations as
fantasy. No special demand for this work came from the public
and no attempt was made by Martin Fuller to advertise it. It was
limited in its sale to those who always keep an eye on the counters
of the bookshops where works dealing with occult and spiritual
subjects are sold. These were the men and women who by word of
mouth created whatever demand there was.

A few of the readers, people who already knew something of
spiritualism or theosophy or were students of occultism, wrote to
James Flanagan expressing their satisfaction in a work that was
so clear and explicit in its description of what life was like on the
Etheric plane. They complimented him for his sound and logical
explanation of life in that realm.

Others, recently bereaved, were moved to send him words of
gratitude for showing them a picture of the plane that was now
the dwelling-place of those they had lost. These spoke of the comfort, hope, and courage the author's revelations had given them.

Flanagan read and re-read these letters, and as he read he marvelled that he, James Flanagan, should be receiving such words

from all points of the compass from strangers who seemed to feel that he had been a torch that illumined their pathway.

But there it all ended.

He and Molly had moved far uptown near a great park into a little apartment which he had furnished very simply out of the generous cheque Mrs. Fuller had given him. But careful and frugal as he had been, these funds were almost spent and the book was having too small a sale to pin any hope to it.

At certain times Cummings would come to Flanagan when the lame man would go to a certain secluded spot in the Park where he might hear his spirit friend's voice without distraction. He was ashamed to tell Cummings of the failure of the book and more so to speak of what was more important to him—the plight he again found himself in for money. No nearer a livelihood than before. He was not even a real author who might pick up a job on a newspaper or turn out light fiction for those popular magazines he used to read.

Flanagan began to lose his courage and his faith in the great mission.

The reason of it all was clear to him. No one *wanted* the masses to know what life after death was like; that is, no one who had the power to get the book before the public as publishers did their well-known authors. Here again it was all dollars and cents. What use was all that work? What good was it to bear that terrible pain in the top of his spine when Cummings was dictating, until he couldn't bear it any longer? And then there were all those hours afterward when he was so weak.

And now it was all for nothing.

What could he tell Molly now? She believed he was a real author, a man in the class of people she looked up to as superior beings.

She had wondered over the mystery of it all and his secretive ways, and sometimes she was a bit unhappy at his changed ways of life.

When the book came out, Flanagan had let her read it. Molly was horrified. So this was what he had been doing! She was frightened, too. She didn't think he was insane now, but she felt that a devil was at the bottom of it all.

Flanagan bore her tears and reproaches and was touched when she prayed so earnestly for him. He was sure that success would win her over in the end.

Through all this, Cummings's frequent visits had kept his heart up, but when he had to report the sales of the book, even Cummings was all but despairing. He knew he would be unable to help Flanagan any further. All that he possessed now was his mind. His affairs had been wound up and his distant cousin had sold his few rare possessions and pocketed the money along with what his mother had left him.

The two were ready to admit that their work had left humanity and Flanagan almost precisely as they were before it was begun.

There was no purpose in trying any further.

CHAPTER XLVI

❖

MARTIN had a dim but grim satisfaction in showing the sales report to his wife. He had brought the book out simply to please her. She wanted to be the saviour of the world. Well, the world didn't wish to be saved. It never had wished to be saved. All human history showed that.

Fuller went home to dinner with a feeling of elation. At last he had gained a victory over Dent Cummings. He didn't quite think of it in that way. He preferred to regard it as a triumph of his business acumen and practical judgment. Dent Cummings had lost in the war, and here he was the loser again; and though he missed him as a friend and in his business, he had been aware that there was a wall between him and his wife beyond which he had never penetrated, and which, his intuition told him, Cummings had. He knew perfectly well that his friend had never been a lover to Doris, but somehow they were mentally together beyond the barrier that his understanding had never been able to pierce.

That evening, after the coffee had been served, he said:

"*Life on the Etheric* is the worst seller on our list."

Martin had tried to make his voice keep to its customary tone as he faced Doris across the table.

"I'm not surprised." Her voice sounded as casual as his, but it was rather colder than usual.

"I thought you expected it would make a terrific sensation." Martin gave his best attention to putting the sugar in his cup.

"I was sure it would be if the public had a chance to know about it."

"You didn't expect me to spend money on an advertising campaign for that class of book?"

"Why not? You've done it for several trashy novels."

"Do I have to apologize for that? The trash is what makes it possible to publish books like *Life on the Etheric*. My God, what a title! How many people know what 'Etheric' means?"

"You could tell them."

"Darling, I'm a publisher, not a schoolmaster." Martin's voice now had a decided ring of triumph.

"Martin, you *wanted* that book to fail. You intended that it should."

Her voice was weary, as though this idea was not new but had often tormented her.

"My dear, I'm not bringing out books for the fun of the thing."

"Did you read that book yourself—I mean really read it, not just skim it?"

"Of course."

"Then don't you care anything about the things it tells us? Don't you see the importance of them?"

"I'm not sure that they make any difference. I'll admit it seems to be pretty good sense. There's logic and even science in what it says. I can even believe it's all true."

"Then why not stand by it?" There was no weariness in her voice now.

"Because the public doesn't *want* to believe anything that's logical. It wants to believe that there is going to be something for nothing in the next world. People don't get it here, so they like to think it will be handed to them in the hereafter. And what do they care about the dead? Everyone mourns his own dead, of course, but after a time people grow resigned. A new generation replaces the ones who were killed in the war and— Well, life goes on, my dear."

"But what about the soldier dead, the ones who can't forget, the ones in torment on the other side?"

"Darling, I'm not a politician. I don't make the wars."

"No, but if they knew, if they understood—"

"My dear Doris, politicians never read anything but their own speeches."

"Then *make* them. Make them read that book. You know how, Martin. You're not going to turn back now. Here is a chance to do a greater thing than make money. It's a chance to save the world from suicide. The people are sick—soul-sick and desperate for something they can cling to. For some hope, some light, something to work for, live by, and die by. They've lost faith in government, in business, even in religion. Like pagans they've turned to beauty for help, but even art is perverted and gives them only ugliness. Most of all they've lost faith in themselves. How can they find a way out? Only by learning that immortality is *true*. Finding out that this life is the pattern we make for the next one. It's the truth about themselves they're groping for. They need to *know* that they have a soul and that it cannot die; that it lives on, but in conditions we are creating *here* and *now* and that what we *believe* is the thing that will bind us or loose us after death just as it does now."

When she paused Martin made no answer. He had forgotten his coffee, but the light in Doris's face seemed too bright to bear and